DEVELOPMENTAL MECHANISMS
OF
VERTEBRATE EYE RUDIMENTS

DEVELOPMENTAL MECHANISMS
OF
VERTEBRATE EYE RUDIMENTS

by

G. V. LOPASHOV

Professor at the Institute of Animal Morphology
of the Academy of Sciences of the U.S.S.R.
Moscow

Translated by

JEAN MEDAWAR

A Pergamon Press Book

THE MACMILLAN COMPANY

NEW YORK

1963

591.48
L 864

THE MACMILLAN COMPANY
60 Fifth Avenue
New York 11, N. Y.

This book is distributed by
THE MACMILLAN COMPANY—NEW YORK
pursuant to a special arrangement with
PERGAMON PRESS LIMITED
Oxford, England.

Set in Modern Number 7-10 on 11 point

MADE IN GREAT BRITAIN

Contents

Translator's Preface

Professor Lopashov's *Developmental Mechanisms in Vertebrate Eye Rudiments* was published in Moscow in 1960.

This translation could hardly have been undertaken without the unsparing help of Professor D. R. Newth at all stages, and I am grateful to Professor Michael Abercrombie, who also read the entire translation, for his helpful comments. My sincere thanks are also due to Mrs. Rosemary Marchant, who undertook the unusually onerous secretarial work, and to Mr. Peter Brennan of Pergamon Press for his careful reading of the manuscript and his many invaluable suggestions.

JEAN MEDAWAR

Introduction
to the English Edition

EACH phase in the history of modern developmental biology has had a characteristic approach to the problems of morphogenesis, but each has found in the vertebrate eye a material well suited to their elucidation. Professor Lopashov's book is thus a contribution to one of the classical fields of experimental embryology and he is building upon foundations laid by many distinguished predecessors. Lewis, Spemann, Mangold, Woerdeman, Twitty, Filatov, Stone, Holtfreter, Dragomirov and others have wrested from the eye some of the most illuminating analyses of the developmental process. It is thus particularly interesting to see how far this material yields to the prevailing approach to morphogenetic problems as exemplified in Professor Lopashov's work. For although this book bears the stamp of its author's own originality in experiment and in conception, and although it is also clearly a product of the community of Soviet embryologists of which he is a foremost member, yet its spirit has much in common with the present trend in experimental morphology in every part of the world.

This trend is characterized by an open-minded willingness to concede importance to factors operating in developmental processes which many of us once tended to relegate to subsidiary rôles. Mechanical stresses, the availability of nutrients, the inter-relationships of cells other than inductive ones, seemed so much less interesting and important than chemo-differentiation effected by "organ-forming substances", or by induction, or represented in gradients. It would, of course, be wholly unfair to suggest that the embryologists working twenty and thirty years ago were unwilling to recognize the extreme complexity of developmental interactions. On the contrary, embryology has always been fortunate in its relative freedom from self-imposed limitations of view. But, with the success of factor-analysis in genetics before them, it was clearly the duty of the embryologists of the time to explore to the full any phenomenon that offered a serious prospect of providing a unified theory of development. As Professor Lopashov makes clear, the new approach to morphogenesis springs directly from limitations in the old which were only revealed by experiments of the greatest refinement and precision.

In reviewing his own work, and that of his colleagues, in relating it to previous work on the eye, and in discussing the development of the eye in the general context of embryonic differentiation, Professor Lopashov has provided us with a stimulating and revealing book. It is not always an easy one. Some of his views on the temporal course of differentiation will not have the virtue of familiarity for many readers of the English edition, but here he is attempting to establish important generalizations in an intrinsically difficult field. It is a common concern to find the most convenient and discriminating experimental situations for testing them. It is to be hoped that workers in other branches of experimental embryology will find his ideas of great heuristic value.

For its review of original work, for its theoretical discussion, and as an example of current Soviet embryological thinking, this translation should be welcomed by the English-speaking embryological world.

D. R. NEWTH

Foreword

IN THIS BOOK an attempt has been made to throw light on certain general problems of causality in development through a study of experimental work on the embryonic vertebrate eye. Future progress in embryology must, of course, depend upon the solution of these problems.

Considerations of space and of presentation have made it impossible to provide a detailed analysis of the literature of eye development, or to deal with any but the most important work.

I am deeply grateful to my colleagues Professor T. A. Dettlaff, Dr. G. M. Ignatieva, and Dr. O. G. Stroeva for their invaluable help in preparing this book for press.

G. V. LOPASHOV

CHAPTER I

Introduction*

1. General Preface

THE PROBLEM of embryology is to discover the fundamental laws governing the development of the individual, and its aim is to understand and to master this remarkable process.

The discovery of causal dependencies in ontogeny must naturally play a leading part in the future progress of embryology, but work in this field is not yet wholly satisfactory, since we lack reliable information on causal relations in development. Furthermore, progress in this field must be based upon sound theoretical foundations.

Our problem will, of course, be solved in stages. During its long domination by descriptive methods, embryology was unable to deal with causal relations, or with the conditions necessary for complete development. Successive stages in ontogeny were described, but the factors responsible for the passage of one stage into the next were not discovered. However, such series of stages were used in the solution of evolutionary problems, and from this it came to be believed that it was sufficient to regard the origin of organs from a historical point of view.

In fact, no progress in the treatment of fundamental problems of biology, including embryology, was possible until the following questions had been answered. What are the links between successive generations of living creatures? Why do organisms of successive generations resemble each other in general outline? The historical causalities suggested by evolutionary study cannot alone explain the course of individual development, because they must always act through the processes which link the generations, and a profound knowledge of these processes is thus necessary for embryology.

At the end of the last century, when genetics and experimental embryology were beginning, first attempts were made to interpret developmental processes. These attempts were partly speculative

---

* With the author's permission this chapter has been shortened in translation.

and partly based on developmental abnormalities, and we can now see many of them as no more than failures to confirm guesses which have themselves been swept away by subsequent research.

Progress in understanding the causality of development could only come from experimentation. Indeed, studies in the physiology of development and in genetics have transformed the whole of our biological thinking. It became clear that to understand how the specific form of the mature organism was consistently achieved, one had to make a causal analysis of the processes which accomplish this. Development began to be seen as a series of intimately linked events, rather than as a mere succession of forms. But while experiments did provide a mass of data demonstrating the inter-relationships of different parts of the growing embryo, this advance in embryology was accompanied by serious shortcomings.

In the early days of experimental embryology, isolated results too often served as the basis of wide generalizations. Despite the accumulation of experimental data these generalizations became ever more empirical, as when, for example, the development of a lens above a grafted eye-cup was seen as an example of a general form of dependent differentiation.

In this way the actual outcome of development was attributed to the action of inductors, of "organizers" or of "fields". When it later seemed clear that these did not exercise specific effects, recourse was had to the specificity of the reacting materials. The general conclusions that were drawn were, however, based upon too superficial an experimental analysis, and they were accepted partly because they were consistent with a mechanistic conception of causality. We shall have occasion to see that such an "objective empiricism" has been misleading and that the common tendency to explain phenomena only in terms of those components that have been well studied is philosophically unsound.

The discovery of more cases of dependent differentiation in a variety of developmental processes led to attempts to found upon them wide generalizations about the causality of development. However, the researches of Spemann and Schotté (1932), Harrison (1933), Holtfreter (1933), Lehmann (1933), Filatov (1934), Schmalhausen (1938) and others soon showed the inadequacy of these conceptions and now the following questions can be raised. Do dependencies of one part of an embryo upon another — however important and widespread they may be — really provide a sufficient basis for understanding development, or must other and equally important components be found? Are known relationships alone capable of forming complex organisms, or do they represent but one aspect of more general mechanisms of development?

The theoretical inadequacy of these concepts consisted in seeing many different developmental relations in terms of a single mechanism. And, in fact it can be shown that in some cases the development of a structure may appear dependent on, or independent of, another part of the embryo according to the experimental situation chosen. Thus a standardized way of asking questions, and a corresponding limitation in experimental design, may predetermine the nature of the results obtained. When workers sought only to discover the phase in the development of some part of the embryo during which it was incapable of self-differentiation, and the time of its later transition to the phase in which self-differentiation was possible, the effects of many important influences on development were left unexplored. Thus the availability of proteins or amino acids to the developing system was once thought to be "indifferent" and of little consequence to the problem of differentiation.

While inductive relations were being discovered, it was, perhaps, excusable to relegate to the "background" all the environment of the induced structure other than the inductor. But if this is done the completion of its organogeny cannot be explained. For the further study of the effects of this environmental "background", grafting experiments have only a limited value, and the method of explanting rudiments comes into its own. With its help we may hope to broaden our enquiry so that instead of asking what influence is exerted by one part of an embryo on another, we may ask, in general terms, what is the totality of conditions that leads to the formation of a typical structure and what are the inter-relations of these conditions.

But can embryology alone provide the answers to our questions or should we turn to a wider range of problems, first of all to those concerned with cell components in relation to inheritance and with the interactions of cells and environment during development? Such problems are certainly, in principle, within the scope of experimental embryology, but in practice embryology has concerned itself until recently far more with the relations between the embryonic layers of cells. However, we must, at least, acknowledge the importance of the problems of the connexion between development and evolution, an acknowledgement which has to avoid the old, but persistent, confusion between the two.

These, then, are the considerations which have decided the nature of the present work. Its purpose is the experimental dissociation of individual components of the complex of conditions that have been regarded as the background for organ development, and an attempt at understanding their development on this basis. Because this problem cannot be solved at once, the work is directed initially to the detection of links between local phenomena and the development of the organ as a whole. The objects of the research are *vertebrate eye rudiments*. Their development is one of the best analysed experimentally (Lopashov and Stroeva 1961). The structure of eyes, differentiated into retina, pigment epithelium and lens, is very clear and allows us to distinguish them under different experimental conditions. All these pecularities, together with its suitability for experiment, determine the choice of the eye as the best model for the aim proposed. Some preliminary communications (Lopashov 1945a, 1946, 1948a, b, 1951 and 1956) will be mentioned later only when especially necessary.

2. Observations on Method

(a) Techniques and Treatment of Material

The usual methods of experimental embryology were used, but they were sometimes applied unusually. Eye rudiments from early embryos, optic vesicles, and pieces of pure neural plate were isolated in saline, either by themselves or with other embryonic tissues, or they were grafted into different parts of the body of normal embryos, or embryos from which a part of the anlage had been removed. This varied series of combinations produced various degrees of completion in the morphogenesis of the eye and provided information about the conditions necessary for its development, and about the properties of the eye rudiment itself.

Ordinary operative techniques were used, and whole embryos and explants were cultured in sterile conditions by the methods described by Holtfreter (1931, 1934a). The embryos were thoroughly washed in alcohol and the membranes were then removed with a sharp steel needle. Steel and glass needles and fine, sharp knives were used for the operations. Holtfreter saline was used as a culture medium for the embryos during the first post-operation day, and for the whole course of development in the case of explants. When it was essential that the embryos should not stick to the bottom of the glass culture vessel, it was coated with a 2 per cent agar solution. One or two embryos and 1–5 explants were cultured in about 10 ml of liquid, so that the volume of fluid medium was much greater than that of the average eye explants, which measured about 0.02 mm³ each. The explants were sketched about once every 24 hours, and were fixed at different periods, so that their progress could be followed in sections. Normal embryos of the same age were used as controls. Some were fixed at the stage when the operation was made, and others simultaneously with the explants; sometimes different series started at the same time were used as controls for each other.

Experiments were always made at room temperature, but in the unfortunate absence of an adequate thermostat this varied considerably from season to season. The explant cultures were kept under observation for up to 16 days, during which time the typical basic structure of the eye was laid down in the controls. Embryos with grafted eyes sometimes lived even longer. It must, however, be remembered that development and structure vary much more in grafted and explanted eyes than they do in normal development. The picture of development is usually, and inevitably, incomplete, because successive stages of eye development are being compared, and some are slightly atypical; but by comparison of the different examples, and by performance of detailed analyses, the typical picture can be worked out. When performing experiments on the interior of the organism we can never fully discover how far general environmental conditions and how far the internal medium affect the development of a particular organ. When eyes, or parts of eyes, are grafted from one embryo to another, some part of the diverse environmental conditions within the organism remains the same, and these conditions, as well as the direct influences exercised by local parts, play an important part in the organization of the rudiment. On the other hand, simple isolation from the organism can only produce a much modified sort of development, which it is impossible to investigate: this development can always be explained by reference to an absence of the "influence of the whole". In fact, these "influences of the whole" are themselves perfectly concrete and definite factors. In order to understand and analyse the factors involved, separate and successive environmental conditions must be examined, both singly and in combination with each other.

How exactly can the eye rudiment be separated into its several components by operation, and what is their behaviour outside the embryo? Histological analysis cannot answer these questions, and in order to solve them it seems to be necessary to employ the old mode of the "anatomy of the living embryo" introduced by von Baer (1828) and other pioneers of embryology. The dissection of embryos with immediate observations upon the behaviour of the eye rudiments and their parts, separated from normal surrounding, give an insight in these questions.

The living material was examined and sketched under binoculars magnifying from 25 times to 120 times. The material was fixed with Bouin, stained with carmine and Blue Black B mixed with picric acid or Orange G. Borax carmine and Mallory's red were used for the later stages. Three species of urodeles and five anurans were used: *Triturus taeniatus* and *T. vittatus*, *Amblystoma mexicanum*, *Rana terrestris (arvalis)*, *R. esculenta*, *R. ridibunda*, *Bufo viridis* and *Pelobates fuscus*. Only the material which developed successfully was used in the quantitative analysis and subsequent descriptions. Four to five control embryos of each stage were used in the analyses of normal development. Further details of the methods are separately set out in each chapter.

(b) Structure of Larval Amphibian Eye and Experimental Results

The normal amphibian eye will always be used as a standard against which to measure the degree of recovery in operated eyes, and it is therefore essential to describe the structure of both the larval eye (Fig. 1 a) and the adult eye (Fig. 1 b). The descriptions are taken from basic accounts of the structure and development of the amphibian eye by Mangold (1931), Walls (1942), Rochon-Duvigneaud (1943), Detwiler (1943) and Winnikov (1947 b), and from original material.

The retina is subdivided into a series of layers. The outer layer is made up of visual cells, whose external surface forms light sensitive outgrowths known as rods and cones which pierce the external limiting membrane bounding the outside of the retina. The next, more internal layer is the inner reticular layer of the retina, which is made up of protoplasmic outgrowths from the visual cells. In the larval amphibian this layer is extremely delicate. The inner nuclear layer lies next: it is several nuclei thick, and separates the inner reticular layer from the ganglionic layer, which is the inner layer of the retina. A thin layer of nerve fibres covers this inner surface, and is separated from the cavity of the eye—which is filled by the vitreous body—by the internal limiting membrane. A delicate web of hyaloid blood vessels covers the membrane in anurans and supplies the inner surface of the retina. These blood vessels are absent in urodeles.

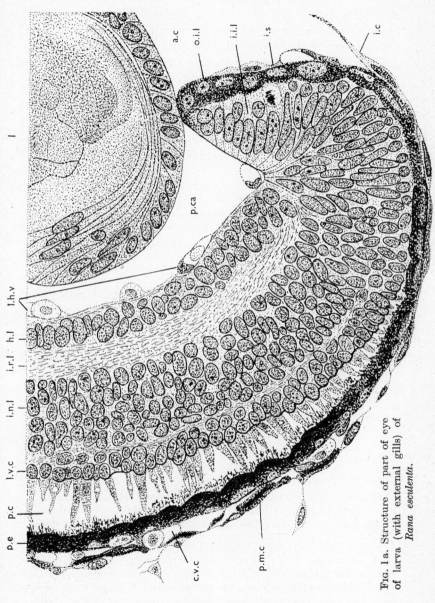

Fig. 1a. Structure of part of eye of larva (with external gills) of *Rana esculenta*.

2*

A heavily pigmented unicellular layer of pigment epithelium forms an outer boundary around the retina. Outgrowths develop from the inner, retinal surface of this layer soon after its completion, and separate the rods and cones from each other.

The retina is cup-shaped. Around the rim or limbus of this cup, the retina and its contiguous pigment epithelium transform into the iris, which extends to the margin of the pupil. The inner layer of the iris is a continuation of the retina: in tadpoles it is built of columnar epithelium which falls off progressively in thickness and in quantity towards the edge of the pupil, where it becomes unicellular. By bending back around the pupil, it is continuous with the outer layer of the

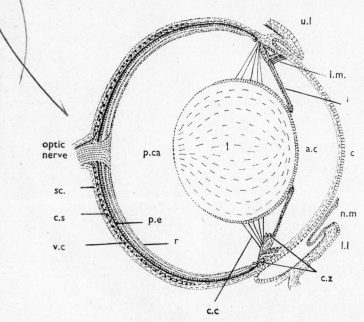

FIG. 1b. Diagram of adult anuran eye (after Walls, 1942). a.c. – anterior chamber of eye, c. – cornea, c.c. – zonule fibres, c.s. – cartilaginous sclera, c.z. – ciliary zone, c.v.c – capillary of choroid coat, h.l. – ganglionic layer, i. – iris, i.c. – inner cornea, i.i.l. – inner iris layer, i. n.l.– inner nuclear layer, i.r.l. – inner reticular layer, i.s. – iris stroma, l. – lens, l.l. – lower lid, l.h.v. – hyaloid vessels, l.v.c – layer of visual cells, l.m. – lens muscles, n.m. – nictitating membrane, o.i.l. – outer iris layer, p.c. – primary cavity of eye, p.ca. – posterior chamber (secondary cavity) of eye, p.e. – pigment epithelium, p.m.c. – primary mesenchyme coat, r. – retina, sc. – sclerotic, u.l. – upper lid, v.c. – choroid coat.

iris; this latter is a continuation of the pigment epithelium and is morphologically indistinguishable from it. The retina, pigment epithelium and both layers of the iris appear as a single sheet of cells. These cells are derived from the primary optic rudiment, which represents the neural part of the eye. At first, this optic vesicle appears as an evagination from the brain anlage; this later inverts to form the optic cup, whose two basic layers give rise to the retina and the pigment epithelium. The fissure-like space between the retina and the pigment epithelium is the remnant of the primary cavity of the embryonic eye. The lens develops within the aperture of the pupil and, unlike the primary embryonic eye, arises from the overlying ectoderm.

The choroid coat lies over the pigment epithelium, and is made up of partly pigmented mesenchyme cells and unpigmented vessel cells. It is continued over the iris, where it lies above the outer layer and forms the iris stroma; the many golden and black chromatophores in the stroma give the eye its characteristic colour and pattern. The outer coat is the sclera which consists of a thin layer of colourless cells, and though it is thin at first, it is also strong, and in tadpoles can be removed intact from the eye (Lopashov, 1949). The sclera continues forward as the inner cornea; it is a very thin layer of colourless flat cells, and stays separate from the outer cornea during the whole larval period in anurans, while in urodeles the inner and outer cornea fuse at the beginning of the larval stage. This arrangement allows the eye of the tadpole to rotate in its orbit. The choroid coat, the iris stroma, the sclera and the inner cornea arise from the loose mesenchyme which surrounds the eye rudiment in the embryo; but since their origin is not always clear, wherever the present investigation throws any light on their derivation, the subject will be discussed.

Quite apart from its size, the larval eye differs from the adult at several points: in the adult the retina is relatively less thick and the detailed structure of the light sensitive elements becomes more elaborate but the vascular coat is thicker and becomes more complicated. The sclera becomes cartilaginous—this happens in urodeles which are still in the larval stage. The inner cornea fuses with the outer, and the outer separates from the skin and becomes part of the structure of the eye; the eyelids and the orbit in which the complicated adult eyeball rotate are developed last of all.

The differences between larva and adult are particularly noticeable in the iris, and the growing ciliary body (Romano, 1936; Rochon-Duvigneaud, 1943; Koloss, 1949; and personal observations). While the cells of the outer layer of the iris—its neural part—are flat and pigmented in the early larva and its inner cells are cylindrical and unpigmented, in the adult these cylindrical cells will be pigmented and flattened. A ring-shaped pupillar sphincter muscle is formed in the outer layer of the iris, while a radial pupillar dilator muscle is formed in its inner layer. Unlike other muscles they are derived from the neural part of the eye. The adult iris stroma is noticeably thicker than the larval. The lens becomes fastened by zonule fibres to the ciliary body inside which muscles effecting the movement of the lens are developing. The radial thickenings of the ciliary processes arise on the inner surface of the iris. The ciliary body develops in the limbus; it nourishes the eye and regulates its internal pressure. Its surface is lined with a double epithelial layer, which is a continuation of the two iris layers; they turn into retina or pigment epithelium as they pass to one or the other surface. All these changes which transform the structure of the larval eye into the adult are associated with metamorphosis.

The pigment epithelium, the outer and inner parts of the iris and the retina are sometimes together called the retina; I have kept to the alternative terminology, and describe as retina only the actual visual parts of the cup. The terms pigment epithelium and iris will be used in their proper sense. Ordinary terminology does not take into account that these are distinct both in structure, function, ability to regulate in regeneration, and in the conditions necessary for their development.

3. Plan of Work

It is impossible to give an account of all the conditions which are necessary for the development of the eye, and at the same time present a picture of their many-sided relationships. Chapters II–IV, therefore, first describe experiments which study only particular aspects of the conditions of development. Then, by passing on to other experiments, the conditions necessary for the development of the eye rudiment are seen from other points of view, and the earlier data may be better understood. Chapter V is devoted to generalizations of the data obtained, first with respect to special regularities of eye development, and then with those of a more general character. The nature of these regularities, as illustrated by research on eye development and on other well known mechanisms of development, is discussed in the sixth and concluding chapter.

CHAPTER II

The Effects of Crowding and of Dispersal on the Cells of the Eye Rudiment

1. Introduction

As ALREADY described, the adjacent layers of the retina and pigment epithelium which compose the main neural part of the eye differ from each other in their development. The retina is thicker and has more layers than the pigment epithelium and, during the development of the rudiment, cells accumulate in the future retina, but spread out into a single layer in the future pigment epithelium. Our first question is: are these contrasting behaviours, crowding and accumulation on the one hand, spreading out on the other, factors in causing the cells to develop either into retina or pigment epithelium? Further, we may ask if this arrangement of the eye material is a necessary condition of its differentiation. For these questions to be answered, the cells must be placed in conditions where they either are crowded or are spread out into a single layer.

2. The Development of the Optic Vesicle in Saline

If the young eye rudiment is explanted into saline the whole of it contracts into a dense mass of cells. This can therefore help us to solve the problem of what happens to the eye rudiment when its cells are crowded together. The experiments were made at the optic vesicle stage. After removal of the covering ectoderm, the rudiments were dissected away from the brain and placed in saline, where they lived for up to 8 days. Of the 112 rudiments used, 31 were from axolotls, 13 from newts, 51 from *Rana arvalis* and 17 from *Bufo viridis*.

Once in the saline, the explants usually stuck to the bottom of the culture vessel, and they seldom became detached during the last days of the culture period. Many wandering cells leave the explant and creep over the surface of the glass. In all the species studied the rudiment developed a similar outline (Figs. 2, 3, 4). At first, it

11

was a single, shapeless, dark grey or brown mass; then, nearly all the explants differentiated into two parts: a large, round, smooth and yellow-white part and a smaller, irregularly shaped part whose size varied and which was sometimes almost totally lacking. In the species with dark eggs—unlike newts—the dark colour is retained in this latter part. This segregation proceeds more slowly in urodeles than in

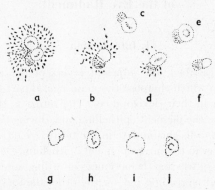

FIG. 2. External view of explant of naked axolotl eye (a–f) and of newt (g–j), after 3 days explantation. The brain pendant can be seen (it is grey in the axolotl). Pigment has accumulated inside the internal fissure cavity (a, c, d, h, j). e shows eye with slight apical invagination.

FIG. 3. External view of naked explanted eye of *Bufo viridis* after 2 day explantation; circulation had started in the control. The brain pendant shows dark. There is a paler coloured patch with a depression at the apex of the eye.

anurans, and the difference between the two parts is not so noticeable. After three days, an inner translucent dark stripe appeared in the paler part of most explants (Figs. 2, 4D). Histological examination showed that whatever its shape may be, the pale part of the explant is without exception entirely made up of retina (Figs. 5–8). Pigment epithelium is absent, for the thinner eye wall, which might have produced it,

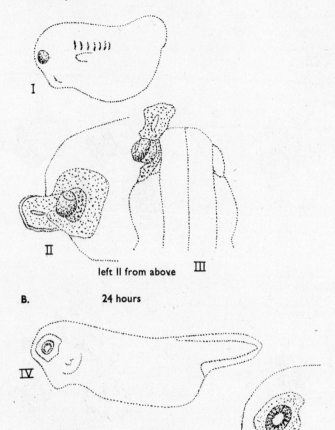

A. Before operation

B.   24 hours

FIG. 4. The development of explants from eye rudiments of *Rana arvalis* compared with controls. A. Embryo before operation. B. Embryo and explants 24 hours after operation. External views of control embryos.

I–V (all except I show eye rudiment exposed) and of explant VI.

48 hours

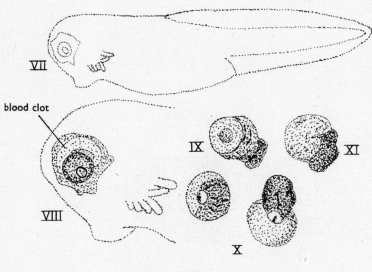

D. 72 hours

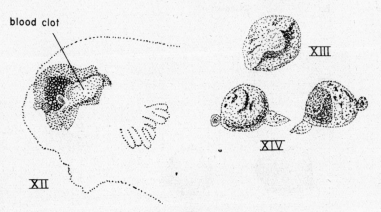

FIG. 4 (continued). C. Control embryos (VII and VIII) and explants
(IX–XI) 48 hours after operation. In IX
there is an invagination at the apex. A dark
brain pendant is seen in IX, X and XI.

D. Control embryo (XII) and explants (XIII
and XIV) 72 hours after operation.

has also developed into retina and is also more or less thickened (Figs. 6, 7); indeed in urodeles this wall becomes as thick as the other one (Fig. 5). The dark stripe which is seen in all the explants is the remnant of the fissure of the primary eye cavity. In this cavity, which is sometimes divided into a series of separate compartments, pigment extruded by the retinal cells accumulates. In some cases, when a lens is being formed by the eye, the fissure disappears, and pigment is extruded through the outer surface of the retina (Fig. 8).

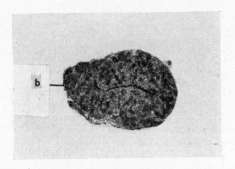

Fig. 5. Transverse section of naked explanted eye rudiment of newt, after 3 days cultivation. Pigment has been extruded into the fissure cavity, b – brain pendant.

This and other influences of the lens on the structure of the eye explants will be discussed in Chapter IV. Fig. 9 shows diagrams of the different types of naked explanted eye rudiments.

The degree of differentiation in the retina varies from species to species. In experiments on newts and axolotls the retina had not differentiated into layers by the time the controls had finished doing so. The visual layer was not distinct, no visual outgrowths developed, and the retina was still made up of deep columnar cells. The concentration of nuclei in a single section was noticeably less in urodeles than in anurans, as could be clearly seen by comparing explants of the same age. The outer reticular layer and the nuclear layers are formed in anurans (Fig. 8), but the visual outgrowths do not differentiate in them.

The dark part of the explant is actually brain tissue which segregates from the eye rudiment after its separation from the brain. Unlike the retinal portion, the size of this brain part varies a great deal. Winnikov

(1947 a, b) described the formation of similar pieces of brain in explants made at the neurula stage; but since Adelmann (1930) and Alderman (1935) found that there was no clearly defined eye rudiment in existence at this stage, Winnikov's experiments cannot prove con-

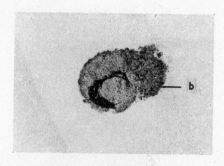

FIG. 6. Transverse section of naked, lens-free, explanted eye rudiment of *Bufo viridis* after 2 days culture. The sickle-shaped fissure cavity contains a large quantity of pigment. b – brain pendant.

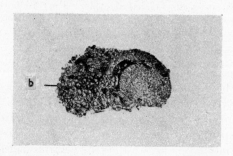

FIG. 7. Transverse section of naked, explanted lensless eye of *Rana arvalis* after 2 days culture. The sickle-shaped fissure cavity contains extruded pigment. b – brain pendant.

vincingly that the brain appendages in his explants came from the anlage of the eye. On the other hand, during the present research it was observed that the appearance of such brain tissue was associated with the development of eye rudiment cells in the brain itself. Furthermore, parts of the brain may arise even from single apical parts of the

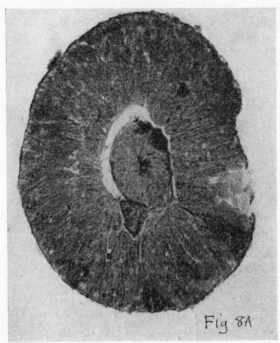

FIG. 8. Transverse sections of explanted eye rudiments of *Rana arvalis*, in which lens material has been left. 8 A is taken after 2 days culture and is shown under higher magnification. 8 B is taken after 4, and 8 c after 6 days culture. The retina is sharply polarized. Pigment can be seen leaving the retina externally. The retina is differentiated into layers in B and C. The retina in c had been prevented from enveloping the lens by being attached to the bottom of the culture vessel.

b – brain pendant, g – glass.

eye rudiment (Chapter IV, section 5). Ikeda's (1935) experiments on the regeneration of the retina from pigment epithelium had earlier showed that such displacements were clearly possible during development.

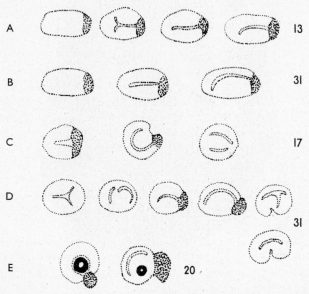

FIG. 9. Diagram of naked, explanted eye rudiments. They are classified according to the thickness of the walls and the disposition of the cavities: A = *Triturus*, B = axolotl, C = *Bufo viridis*, D = *Rana arvalis* without a lens and E = *Rana arvalis* with a lens. The brain pendant is shown by a stippled area, and the lens in black. The figures on the right refer to the numbers operated.

The Emergence of Cells from Explants

In addition to these pieces of brain tissue, the eye explants at first gave rise to many migrating cells which became distributed around them on the glass (Fig. 2). In anurans the number varies from 20 to 100 per explant, but in urodeles, and particularly newts, there are far fewer, and in axolotls not more than 40. There are occasional urodele explants from which no cells emerge. Migrating cells leave the explants right up to the time at which they separate into optic and brain pendant parts, and by the end of 24 hours a zone of creeping cells has already formed around the explant. Winnikov (1945), Holtfreter (1947, 1948b), Niu (1947, 1954) and Algard (1953) have all followed the differentiation of such migrant cells in detail, and no separate study was therefore made here, but it was noticed that the whole population was united by a delicate film, which extended beyond its periphery. This film, together with the wandering cells, whose collective product this film seems to be, could be lifted intact from the bottom of the culture vessel.

It is still unsafe to assume that these facts provide firm support for the idea that migratory cells are derived from the eye rudiment in normal development. Bartelmez (1954), however, showed that a considerable number of cells left the surface of the human eye during normal development, and that these became part of the mesenchyme coat of the eye. Here, as in the experiments already described, these cells could be regarded as a source of the neural mesenchyme, or ectomesenchyme, which is principally derived from the neural folds and the neural crest which is formed at their closure (Harrison, 1938b; Lopashov, 1945b; Hörstadius, 1950). Its cells can, however, also arise from parts of the neural plate—particularly in certain experimental conditions—as Raven (1937), Lopashov (1944) and Niu (1954) showed for its pigment cell component.

It is possible that ectomesenchyme cells leave the eye rudiment under normal circumstances, and that this migration is intensified when the rudiment is separated from the brain. At all events the number of cells which emerge, particularly in urodele amphibians, is not very significant, and the present data are not sufficient to decide what part they play in the formation of the mesenchyme coat.

Our experimental results show that in a fluid medium, where the cells of the rudiment are crowded into a mass with thick walls, the whole rudiment invariably develops into retina, both in urodeles and anurans. The degree of differentiation achieved varies from species to species. In saline the anuran rudiment differentiates into layers—though the visual layer and its outgrowths are not formed—but the urodele rudiment does not.

The experiments did not, however, establish whether or not the development of the retina from the eye rudiment depends solely upon its cells being crowded or also on other environmental conditions which may act by suppressing the development of pigment epithelium. Further experiments which are discussed in later sections were therefore designed.

3. Experiments with Pieces of Anterior Neural Plate
Explanted with Ectoderm in Free-swimming Conditions

If it is true that the development of the retina is connected with the crowding together of the cells in the rudiment, it is likely that either all or a large proportion of these cells will develop into pigment epithelium if their environment obliges them to spread out into a thin layer. Such conditions were obtained when pieces of the anterior half of the neural plate were taken from urodeles at the neurula stage and were explanted in coats of abdominal ectoderm of the same age. In such conditions the developing brain and eye rudiments undergo an intense swelling. In urodele neurulae the ectoderm can easily be freed from all mesoderm cells. The experiments are summarized in Table 1. The edges of the ectoderm quickly united with the edges of the neural plate, and as the latter rolled up into a tube (Holtfreter, 1939, showed that this went on vigorously, even in isolated pieces), the ectoderm was drawn together under it, and in most cases the edges became apposed, and grew together; this produced an explant entirely enclosed by a covering of epidermis. The experiments only take into account entirely closed explants which have been freely swimming in the fluid medium during the whole of their life *in vitro*.

TABLE 1

Variations of the Experimental Method, and its
Application to Various Amphibian Species

Type of experiment	Species		
	Triturus taeniatus	Axolotl	Total
A¹. Anterior half of neural plate, without neural folds or substratum, and abdominal ectoderm	5	20	25
A². Anterior half of neural plate, without folds, and with substratum and abdominal ectoderm	13	6	19
B. Anterior half of neural plate, with folds and abdominal ectoderm	2	19	21
C. Anterior half of neural plate with folds and with mesoderm of the body and abdominal ectoderm	–	6	6
Total	20	51	71

The experiments were able to establish some of the peculiarities which characterize the development of enclosed, free-swimming explants. These are still dense 24–72 hours after operation, and sections of 3-day or younger explants show that the tissues are then tightly packed (Fig. 10). In controls of the same age, two layers of different

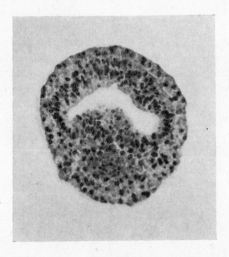

FIG. 10. Structure of the optic part of a 21-day explant of anterior half of neural plate with neural folds and abdominal ectoderm. The eye rudiments are hollow outgrowths with the retinal area unthickened. The tissues are not much differentiated, and lie closely against each other (axolotl).

thickness are already distinguishable, but the thin layer of the pigment epithelium is still colourless. Later on the explants swell to some extent and become semi-transparent, and when they are seen by transmitted light the brain and the eye appear similar both in size and appearance (Fig. 11, A and B).

Eyes always developed from these explants only in the series in which the neural plate was explanted with the neural folds. When the neural folds were separated from the plate and separately explanted, eyes developed either in the substance of the plate, or—particularly in axolotls—in the material of the neural folds, as Mangold (1933a), and Hörstadius and Sellman (1946) demonstrated. The experiments in which the explants were made with the neural folds were therefore most relevant to the problems, particularly so because the greatest enlargement of the brain, and of the eye which arose from its anterior part, was observed in these explants.

The eyes which developed from the explants form a series, graded according to the extent of the swelling they have undergone. The series starts with large vesicles of pigment epithelium in which there

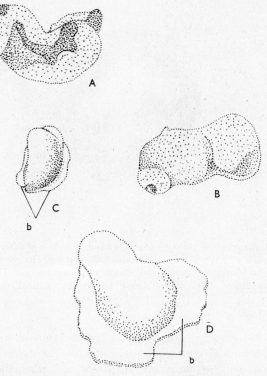

Fɪɢ. 11. External view of explants of axolotl anterior neural plate enclosed by ectoderm, taken when the tissues are fully differentiated (after 7–11 days explantation). A and B are freely swimming explants. C and D are explants developing attached to the glass. b – membrane.

are no traces of retina; next are vesicles in which the walls are dotted with clumps of retinal cells, which sometimes consist of a single layer of unpigmented cylindrical cells and sometimes of several layers (Fig. 12). There may be from 1 to 3 such retinal patches (Fig. 13), and they are sometimes partially merged into one another. In the next group a considerable part of the eye is made up of retina, but the amount of pigment epithelium is all the same disproportionately large, and the two are separated by a considerable space. Lastly there are the eyes in which the retina is, as is normal, closely surrounded

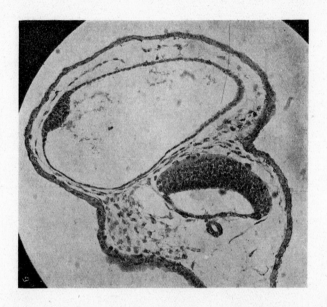

Fig. 12. The eye rudiment has developed as a vesicle of pigment epithelium in which there is a small patch of unpigmented cylindrical cells. The explant was taken from the anterior half of an axolotl neural plate, with neural folds and ectoderm and is shown after 12 days explantation. Brain and epiphysis shown below right.

by a layer of pigment epithelium. Table 2, column 1, shows the frequency and distribution of the series in experiments on axolotls in which the anterior half of the neural plate was explanted with the neural folds and without substratum. Similar results are obtained in experiments in which axial mesoderm was added to the explanted neural plate and neural folds.

The relationship between brain and eye shows a series of variants. The eye, usually single, is occasionally partially bifurcated, and resembles the more anterior termination of the brain. The cavity of

3*

the enlarged eye always retains a direct link with the brain cavity. The pigmented epithelium cells usually pass directly into brain cells (Fig. 13); in two cases the region of transition appears as a tube of pigmented cells, which apparently corresponds to the pedicle of the eye. A variable amount of retinal material is developed in the vesicle-

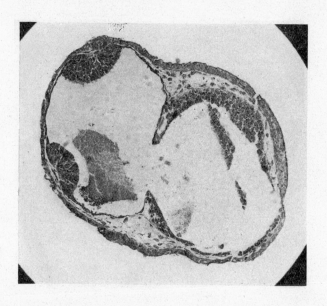

FIG. 13. To the left is shown an eye rudiment in the form of a large vesicle of pigment epithelium with two small retinas; to the right, the vesicle is turning into brain; the material was taken from the anterior half of an axolotl neural plate, with folds and ectoderm, and is shown after 11 days explantation.

like eyes. In seven cases there was one patch, in three there were two, and in one case three patches, and their position in the eye also varied. The degree of differentiation depends both on the period spent in culture and on the thickness of the patch. Given long culture periods, the thicker patches differentiate into reticular and nuclear layers, and visual outgrowths develop on their inward-facing surfaces. The small thickenings (Fig. 12) of two to three layers are unpigmented and undifferentiated. In such explants the cells of the pigment epithelium are very flattened, and in comparison with control embryos, even younger ones, the degree of pigmentation achieved is always low.

The eye always enlarges when the anterior half of the neural plate is explanted with the neural folds. Explants of the anterior quarter or eighth of the plate without the folds (Chapter III, section 2) do not enlarge noticeably. Enlargement or swelling is evidently associated with the presence of large amounts of brain and the fluid secretions which are mainly formed by its ependymal layer (Weiss 1934), and with the presence of neural mesenchyme, which, like the pigment cells, is derived from the neural folds (Hörstadius 1950). In explants which include the folds, it is always more marked, and there are also more pigment cells; when the folds are absent, the amount of mesenchyme is negligible and there are no pigment cells. Holtfreter (1939, 1944) found that this mechanism of swelling was common to epithelial tissues which are surrounded by mesenchyme. A marked enlargement of the brain anlage takes place simultaneously with the swelling of the explanted eyes and leads to changes in the course of its differentiation (Lopashov 1945a).

Similar observations were made by Boterenbrood (1958) in experiments which dissociated and combined cells from the anterior part of the neural plate of early *Triturus* neurulae with pieces of ectoderm: the variations in proportions extended to the point at which the eye rudiment developed into a vesicle of pure pigment epithelium. She also found that development into pigment epithelium was dependent on the accumulation of fluid, and the stretching of tissues of the rudiment.

In this way, depending on the amount of swelling in the eye rudiment and of the stretching of its walls into a thin layer, the proportions of retina and pigment epithelium can vary up to the point where the whole rudiment turns into pigment epithelium. The fact that the retina arises in varying amounts, and in different positions, in the vesicle-like eye shows that up to the stage at which the explants are made there is no localization whatever of the presumptive eye material into retina or pigment epithelium. It seems likely that the zoning develops where the cells of the eye rudiment have become crowded, and where local conditions promote crowding in this particular region of the eye and not in another.

4. Experiments with Explants of Anterior Half of Neural Plate and Ectoderm, Developing Attached to Glass Culture Vessel

The hypothesis that the concentration of cells is an essential factor in the development of the retina may be tested by culturing explants, similar to those just described, in artificially crowded conditions. When such explants are pressed on to the bottom of the culture vessel, some part of each of them remains stuck to the glass for the

TABLE 2

Types of Eye which Develop from Explants of Anterior Half of Neural Plate and their Frequency in Free Swimming Explants and Explants Attached to Glass Culture Vessel

Tissues developed in the explants	Diagram of the eye	I Swimming explants		II Attached explants	
		No. of explants	% of total swimming explants	No. of ex-plants	% of total attached explants
(a) Pure pigment epithelium		2	9.1	—	—
(b) Vesicle of pigment epithelium with some retinal material		11	50	—	—
(c) Retina with swollen pigment epithelium		7	31.8	—	—
(d) Eye with pigment epithelium, and contiguous retina, as in normal organs		2	9.1	9	100

whole of their development. A mass of ectoderm spreads out in a film over the glass around these "sedentary" explants; they never enlarge, but remain covered by tightly stretched ectoderm (Fig. 11, C and D). Only material from axolotls was used in these experiments, and the uniformity of their results is an index of their reliability (Table 2).

The structure of the eye and brain in these explants was quite typical, and devoid of any swelling (Fig. 14 A). The eye is made up of a cup-shaped retina, attached to a lens of normal shape and size, and is closely surrounded by pigment epithelium (Table 2, II). If the explants became attached to the glass over a large area of the under surface of the brain, two eyes, with lenses, arose at the anterior end; but in one explant, in which only a small part of the brain was attached to the glass, the eyes were only half separated, and a single unpaired nasal placode lay in front of them. In these examples the glass was fulfilling the function usually performed by the median part of the mesodermal substrate (Mangold, 1931; Adelmann, 1937; Lehmann, 1937, 1938). Where the eye comes into direct contact with the glass, the pigment epithelium lacks pigment, and merges with the retina.

These experiments indicate that when the material of the eye rudiment is crowded, the main mass develops into retina, the pigment epithelium becomes only a thin layer outside it, and the structure and proportions of the layers are normal. They also stress the importance of the tightly stretched embryonic epidermal ectoderm in restricting the space in which the development of the brain and eye rudiment occurs.

5. The Development of the Lens and Auditory Vesicle in Free-swimming and Sedentary Explants

Both lenses and auditory vesicles developed in the explants described in the two previous sections. Without going into details, I should like to note the importance of phenomena revealed for eye development for an understanding of the development of these organ rudiments.

The frequency of lens formation varies according to the type of operation, and to the species used (Table 3). This table refers only to specimens with well-developed retinas, and in free-swimming explants these were sometimes absent. It is well known that in axolotl lenses very seldom develop when pieces of eye vesicle are grafted under ectoderm of the same stage, while in similar experiments (Sheina,

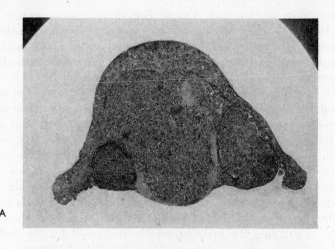

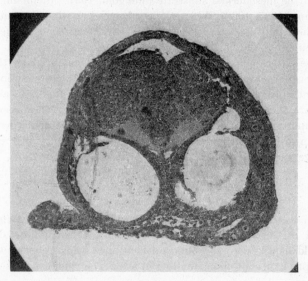

FIG. 14. The explant has developed attached to the glass, and this restricts the space required for the development of internal rudiments. The structure of the eyes (A) is typical; there is no pigment epithelium at the point of contact with the glass; the auditory vesicles (B) are large and subdivided; the brain is compact. The material is from the anterior half of axolotl neural plate with folds and ectoderm, and is shown after 15 days explantation.

1944) using late gastrula ectoderm, they developed in 83.3 per cent of cases. Experiments on a somewhat later stage showed that lenses developed in 25 per cent of the swollen explants which were described earlier, and that in explants of neural folds with ectoderm covering, in which the connexion between the eye material and the ectoderm was not broken, 57 per cent developed lenses; however, when contact was enforced between the eye rudiment and the ectoderm, lenses developed in 100 per cent of cases, which emphasizes the importance of close contact in lens induction.

TABLE 3

Frequency of Appearance of Lenses under Various Culture Conditions

Species	Type of experiment								
	Free-swimming explants of neural plate with abdominal ectoderm			Free-swimming explants of neural folds with surrounding ectoderm			Sedentary explants of neural plate with abdominal ectoderm		
	No. of explants	Explants with lenses	% of explants with lenses	No. of explants	Explants with lenses	% of explants with lenses	No. of explants	Explants with lenses	% of explants with lenses
Triturus	11	5	45	10	10	100	—	—	—
Axolotl	20	5	25	14	8	57	9	9	100

The frequency with which the auditory vesicle appears, and its structure, also varies according to the type of experiment and to the species. In free-swimming explants of newt neural plate which lack a mesodermal substrate, and may or may not have neural folds, the ectoderm develops either large auditory vesicles which lie beneath the brain, or a continuous chain of them which immediately surround the neural tube; similar explants from axolotls develop only from one to five very small vesicles. When such newt explants include underlying mesoderm, then two large vesicles develop on the margin of the mesoderm. In axolotls two vesicles are formed in the same way, but they are larger than in the explants without mesoderm; all are, however, simple and unpartitioned vesicles.

Axolotl explants which are developing on glass develop vesicles which are very different from these: two large partitioned auditory vesicles develop symmetrically on either side of the brain (Fig. 14 B). In the explants described earlier, in which only small areas were attached to the bottom, the structure of the ear vesicles was more complicated. In this way, the intensity of the contact—as in the case of the lens—strongly affects both the size and differentiation of the vesicle; this is evident from a comparison of the vesicles in free-swimming and attached axolotl explants—including those which contain mesoderm, in which the vesicles are much larger. Species peculiarities in ear vesicle forming capacity of ectoderm in the experiments described, correspond to the data of Kogan (1940) and Ginsburg (1946 c).

6. The Importance of Space Restriction and of Ectodermal Tension in Normal Eye Development

In order to confirm and control the results of the original observations and to examine the part played by these regularities in normal development, further experiments were set up. In these experiments R. arvalis and R. esculenta were used to examine the effects of the pressure within the eye rudiment, and the restricting effect of the head ectoderm.

If the ectoderm is carefully removed from the head of an embryo at the optic vesicle stage, the rudiment enlarges rapidly and noticeably on the exposed side of the head. The constriction between the cavity of the eye rudiment and the brain (which marks the position of the future eye stalk) is lost, and the brain passes into an ill-defined eye (Fig. 4, A, II). It seems likely, then, that at the optic vesicle stage, the shape of the eye and the formation of the constriction which separates it from the brain already depend upon the pressure exerted by the surroundings of the eye, while the pressure inside the eye makes it expand. The normal size and shape of the eye thus depend upon the correlation of these two influences. Chanturishvili (1942) made similar experiments, and found that when one eye was punctured the other failed to enlarge. At this stage then the fluid which fills the general cavity of the eye and brain is already under pressure.

Comparison with experiments on explants shows that the effects of this internal pressure are also felt at later stages. Enlargement in the explants begins at the stage when the walls of the control eyes are already of unequal thickness (Chapter II, section 3). Evidently the conditions which in urodeles cause the cells of the eye rudiment to crowd together are still required in these stages in order that a large number of them can form retina. This follows from the fact that in the majority of cases in which enlargement is delayed the eyes develop into vesicles consisting almost entirely of pigment epithelium.

Comparison of these experiments with the basic experiments on explants shows that the shape of the eye rudiments, their separation from the brain, and normal proportions of retina and pigment epithelium are dependent on ectodermal tension, and the consequent restriction of the space in which the eye rudiment is formed. These factors oppose the internal pressure of the eye rudiment.

The experiments described in this chapter have demonstrated the importance of crowded conditions for the development of the eye rudiment cells into retina, and the importance of their being stretched into a single layer for the development of pigment epithelium. The experiments, at the same time, did not explain why pigment epithelium developed in the enclosed explants, where space was very restricted, while it was absent from the eyes which were developing in a fluid medium. These problems, with others, are examined in the next chapter.

CHAPTER III

The Function of the Mesenchyme and Blood Supply in the Segregation of the Eye Rudiment

1. Introduction

THE BASIC problem with which the experiments described in this chapter are concerned, is to discover the function of the mesenchyme in the development of the eye rudiment. In early stages the rudiment is surrounded by a layer of loose mesenchyme which later forms the choroid coat, iris stroma, sclera and inner cornea, all of which become part of the developing eye. After blood has entered the choroid coat, the coat becomes a new source of nourishment for the growing eye. It might therefore be expected that the formation of the whole eye and the differentiation of the rudiment into its component parts, are affected both by the formation of the coats and by the establishment of the vascular supply.

The possible significance of the mesenchyme has already been considered in a preceding chapter. Pigment epithelium never develops when the explants are cultured in a fluid medium, but always develops in closed explants. The closed explants differ in that they always contain mesenchyme, which is in contact with the surface of the eye rudiment just where the pigment epithelium develops. Finally, in the sites where closed explants of eye rudiment stick to the glass (Chapter II, section 4), the presumptive pigment epithelium develops into retina and becomes incorporated into the normal retinal tissues. None of these facts is alone sufficient for an assessment of the part played by the mesenchyme in the development and differentiation of the eye rudiment and its pigment epithelium; further special experiments are therefore needed.

Since the importance of the lenses and of the ectoderm from which they develop for the formation of the eye is discussed in the next chapter, this section will describe experiments on eyes from which lens-forming material has been removed. The formation of the eye coats and of the blood supply alters the relationship of the eye rudiment to the surrounding medium, just as does the aggregation of the cells into a single mass or their arrangement into a thin layer. The causes of alterations in the fate of cells according to their position in relation to the medium are also discussed.

2. The Development of Eye Rudiments explanted in Ectodermal Coats, either without Mesenchyme or with Mesenchyme from Various Sources

Explants of eye rudiment taken at the optic vesicle stage were set up in various combinations in order to determine the part played by the mesenchyme in the development of the pigment epithelium and in the differentiation of the retina. Some were enclosed in ectoderm from neurulae completely freed from mesoderm cells, others were similarly enclosed in ectoderm, but a layer of mesoderm cells was included; in five cases this layer was replaced by prechordal head mesoderm. In a third set the rudiments were enclosed in coats of cleaned ectoderm together with a piece of head neural fold which acts as a source of mesenchyme and fills the explant. In a fourth series the explants were enclosed in ectoderm taken from the heads of embryos at the optic vesicle stage; in these the source of ectomesenchyme was the neural crest which was taken undamaged by the operation. In a fifth series the ectoderm enclosed small pieces of anterior neural plate, without neural folds, and this material corresponded roughly to the future eye rudiments with a small piece of brain behind them; these pieces contain about an eighth of the length of the neural plate.

The mesenchyme was of different kinds, in order to discover the significance of its source of origin for the formation of the pigment epithelium and mesenchymal eye coats. It has been quite clearly shown that ectomesenchyme (from the neural folds, and, later, from the neural crest) and mesodermal mesenchyme differ in their fate, and in particular in the roles they play in the formation of the different rudiments (Chapter V, section 3). Barden (1942) found that the pigment cells which lie in the iris of larval amphibia are, like all larval chromatophores, derived from the neural folds, but apart from this very little is still known about the origin of the various components of the eye coats.

A total of 143 experiments was made on newts, axolotls, *R. arvalis* and *R. ridibunda*.

Explants of Eye Rudiments in Ectodermal Coats

The object of these experiments was to examine the effect of isolating the eye rudiment from the saline medium by ectoderm which had been completely divested of mesenchyme cells. However, mesenchyme was discovered in all anuran explants and occasionally in explants from urodeles. This mesenchyme evidently comes from the migratory cells which emerge from the eye rudiment after it has separated from the brain (Chapter II, section 2; Chapter III, section 2). The fact that there was much more of it around bare explants of anuran eyes than around urodele eyes is supported by observing that it is always present in anuran explants of the present series. These experiments may be used to estimate the relation between the development of pigment epithelium and the presence or absence of mesenchyme. As can be seen from Table 4, it is equally clear that while pigment epithelium does not form if mesenchyme is absent, the mere presence of mesenchyme is not enough to cause its formation. A comparison of the different examples shows that it forms only when there is a sufficient amount of mesenchyme and when there is a firm contact between it and the eye. The mesenchyme lies mainly attached to the outer wall of the explants. Thus pigment epithelium forms where the explant lies close to this wall, but does not develop in every part of the eye which is reached by mesenchyme.

TABLE 4

Frequency of Formation of Pigment Epithelium in relation to Presence or Absence of Mesenchyme in Explants

Species	No. of explants	Mesenchyme		Pigment Epithelium	
		Present	Absent	Present	Absent
Triturus	10	2	8	0	10
Axolotl	10	5	5	1	9
R. arvalis	5	5	0	4	1
R. ridibunda	7	7	0	7	0

The structure of urodele eye rudiments without mesenchyme exactly resembles their structure if developing in a fluid medium, though the cavity is considerably larger (Fig. 15). This is probably related to the fact that even in explants without added sources of mesenchyme there are nevertheless isolated mesenchyme cells present which lead to the formation of basal membranes in the ectoderm. This leads in turn to the retention of a cavity in the ectodermal coat, and to the accumulation of fluid in it which produces the enlargement of the eyes. Again, eye rudiments which develop in the absence of mesenchyme are very like those which develop from explants of ectoderm

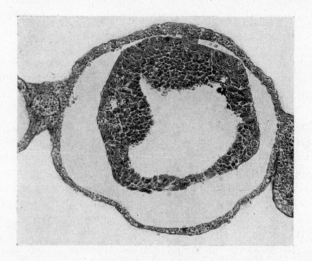

FIG. 15. The newt eye rudiment has developed into a vesicle of retinal material without pigment epithelium. Pigment is entering the cavity of the eye. There are no mesenchyme cells in the cavity of the ectodermal vesicle. The explanted eye vesicle was wrapped in ectoderm from a neurula. Taken after 8 days explantation.

under the influence of foreign inductors, in which mesenchyme also does not develop (Lopashov, 1936; Yamada and Takata, 1955a; Hayashi, 1956). It is obvious that the absence of mesenchyme is in some way responsible for the atypical structure of these eyes. In nearly half the experiments on newts and axolotls (not included in Table 4), the optic rudiments came out of their ectodermal coats in 24–48 hours. These were probably cases in which there was a complete absence of mesenchyme, and the ectoderm, for this reason, did not form a vesicle but remained as a friable ball of cells (Holtfreter, 1934c; 1938a, b, c).

These experiments clearly show that ectomesenchyme is essential for the origin of the pigment epithelium. Special experiments are needed in order to decide whether or not mesenchyme of a different origin can produce the same result.

Experiments on Explanting Eye Rudiments with Sources of Mesoderm and Ectomesenchyme from the Neurula Stage

In assessing these experiments it must be remembered that, especially in anurans, the mesodermal mesenchyme may be mixed with the neural mesoderm which emerges from the eye rudiment. The explants develop into small closed vesicles; inside is a network of mesenchyme of varying thickness in which the eye rudiments lie; they are easily visible to external inspection after 3–4 days when the explants become transparent. Some of the explants became attached to the bottom of the culture glass, as has been described in earlier experiments (Chapter II, section 4).

The results are most easily understood if the explanted rudiments are classified into a series based on the development of the pigment epithelium, the disposition of the inner cavity of the eye and the shape of the retina. The development of the pigment epithelium and of other features of the eye varies with the species and with the occurrence of mesenchyme of particular kinds. These different types of eyes are shown diagrammatically in Table 5.

Figs. 16–20 show the differentiation of urodele eye rudiments in the presence of mesoderm. Although ectomesenchyme is always mixed with the mesodermal mesenchyme in the explants, the latter can be distinguished, particularly in urodeles, by its forming mainly strands and layers similar to those which line the body cavity (Figs. 16, 17, 18), closed vesicles resembling vessels (Fig. 17), and occasionally blood cells. Pure ectomesenchyme, on the other hand, usually develops into a loose network and only forms sheets when it bounds a cavity. At first these sheets are found lining the ectoderm. Even in explants which have been provided with both sources of mesenchyme the total quantity of mesenchyme actually formed is small and always insufficient to fill more than a part of the volume of the explant.

In explants containing mesodermal mesenchyme from newt embryos pigment epithelium is formed in 25 per cent of cases and in similar explants of axolotl embryos it forms in 53·8 per cent of cases. In explants containing ectomesenchyme it arises in 53·8 per cent of cases among newts and 93·3 per cent among axolotls.

TABLE 5

Frequency of Appearance of Different Types of Eye in Ectodermal Explants in the Presence of Mesenchyme of Different Origins

Type of eye structure	Diagrammatic examples	With mesodermal mesenchyme			With ectomesenchyme		
					From neurula		From eye vesicle stage
		Triturus	Axolotl	Frog	Triturus	Axolotl	Axolotl
A. Retina alone, no pigment epithelium		10 + 2*	6	1	6	1	0
B. Scattered patches (1-3) of pigment epithelium between retinal patches		4	7	1	5	3	2

C. Vesicle of pigment epithelium; 1–2 retinal patches (with an occasional patch of brain) in the walls	10	8	2	3	0	0
D. More or less cup shaped retina. (1–2) covered by pigment epithelium	2	3 + 2*	0	7	0	0
E. More or less cup shaped retina with unenclosed pigment epithelium along edges	0	0	0	4	0	0
Total	14	15 + 2*	13	16	13	14 + 2*

* These explants developed while growing attached to the bottom of the culture vessel; this produced stretching in the ectoderm, and restriction of the internal space.

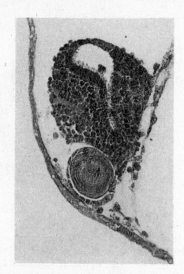

FIG. 16. Newt eye rudiment covered in neurula ectoderm and with flank mesoderm, after 10 days explantation. A secondary lens has developed. The basic retinal layers and the visual cells on the surface of the inner cavity of the eye have both differentiated.

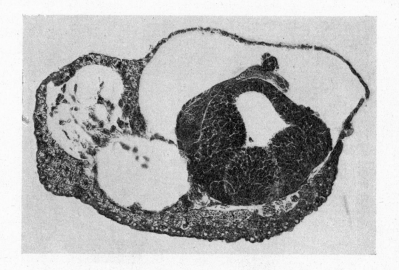

FIG. 17. Eye rudiment of newt, covered in neurula ectoderm and containing prechordal mesoderm, after 7 days explantation. The eye cavity resembles the shape of a brain cavity. The mesenchyme forms a layer with closed loops. There is a dumb-bell shaped lens above (the section shows only its left half) which overlies the thin part of the eye.

4*

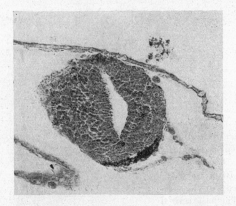

FIG. 18. Eye rudiment, wrapped in neurula ectoderm and with lateral mesoderm, after 10 days explantation. The fissure cavity divides the two walls of retinal material. There is some pigment epithelium at the lower edge of the fissure cavity. Pigment is entering the cavity. The mesenchyme forms strands which approach the eye closely.

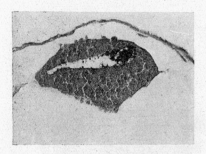

FIG. 19. Axolotl eye rudiment, enclosed in neurula ectoderm with lateral mesoderm, after 8 days explantation. The fissure cavity lies between walls of retina. Pigment can be seen entering it.

FIG. 20. Eye rudiment of axolotl, with pieces of lens ectoderm at the apex, enclosed in neurula ectoderm with lateral mesoderm, after 9 days explantation. Portions of pigment epithelium can be seen at one edge of the fissure cavity. The mesenchyme forms ties and a network, which at some points come close to the eye.

We may compare these figures with those obtained from experiments
in which the eye rudiment was cultured with ectoderm alone, and
in which such small quantities of ectomesenchyme as formed came
from the rudiments themselves. In these cases no newt explants and
but 20 per cent of the axolotl ones developed a pigment epithelium.
Thus we see that the frequency of appearance of pigment epithelium
in the explants rises with the amount of mesenchyme they contain,
and ectomesenchyme is more effective in promoting this appearance
than is mesodermal.

The small amount of mesenchyme in the explants shows that the
formation of pigment epithelium depends not only on the quantity
present, but also on its position in relation to the parts of the eye.
The mesodermal elements often approach the eye very closely
(Figs. 16, 17, 18). The network of ectomesenchyme does not usually

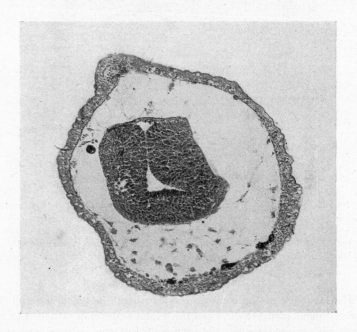

FIG. 21. Newt eye rudiment, enclosed in neurula ectoderm, with
neural fold, after 10 days explantation. At the end of the narrow
fissure cavity the retinal walls join a layer of pale grey pigment epithelium.
The mesenchyme forms a net which approaches the eye above and
below.

lie so close, but is arranged around or beside the eye, and sends out extracellular strands which fasten to its surface. Where pigment epithelium is formed, either these strands come up to it, or separate mesenchyme cells lie on its surface. Careful examination shows that the cell bodies do not form a continuous layer, but the strands from the cells fuse to form an unbroken film on the surface of the pigment epithelium, similar to the film which forms when ectomesenchyme creeps over glass (Chapter II, section 2). Pigment epithelium does not arise if this film is absent.

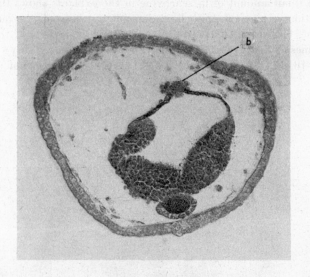

FIG. 22. Newt eye rudiment enclosed in neurula ectoderm, with neural fold, after 10 days explantation. The eye cavity is enlarged, and is bounded on one side by pigment epithelium, in whose substance brain cells are found. A thin mesenchyme net lies close to the pigment epithelium, on whose surface separate mesenchyme cells are found. b – brain cells.

The intimacy of the connexion between the mesenchyme and the eye rudiment is increased when the explants develop attached to the glass and are consequently very compact. But even in these conditions (Fig. 24), the original network of cells does not lie close against the eye, but surrounds it at a distance as a continuous layer, from which a network of strands passes inwards to the eye, uniting with its surface cells. The area of pigment epithelium is greatly augmented in such cases. It is clear that the increased extent of the contact between mesenchyme and eye rudiment produced by the explant's adherence to the glass intensifies the former's influence on the formation of pigment epithelium.

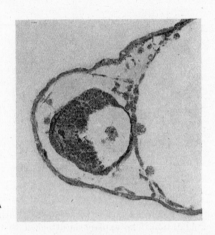

A

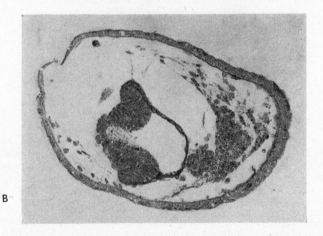

B

FIG. 23. Eye rudiments (A and B) of axolotl, enclosed in neurula ectoderm, with neural folds, after 9 days explantation. The eyes have a cavity shaped like a brain cavity. Two retinas have developed in each. The mesenchyme forms a net. The visual outgrowths are starting to differentiate. The pigment epithelium is grey.

Eye Rudiments Explanted with Mesenchyme Sources of the Same Age

In these experiments the ectoderm with the adherent eye rudiments was removed from the head of the embryo and the rudiments were then separated from the brain at their point of connexion. Both eyes

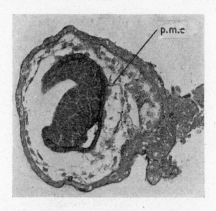

FIG. 24. Axolotl eye rudiment enclosed in ectoderm with neural fold, after 9 days explantation. The explant is attached to the glass. The retina is strongly cupped. The mesenchyme net lies closely against the pigment epithelium. p.m.c. – primary mesenchyme coat.

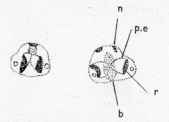

FIG. 25. External view of eyes, explanted with neural mesenchyme of the same age, into head ectoderm, without separating the rudiments from the ectoderm. r – retina, p.e. – pigment epithelium, b – brain, n – nasal placode.

were then freed from the ectoderm, and one was rewrapped in it. These experiments contrast with those of the parallel series in which the eyes were not separated from the ectoderm (Chapter IV, section 3); some of the data from the latter series are taken into account here. Fig. 25 shows the external appearance of the explants from this parallel series.

In explants supplied with ectomesenchyme of the same age, more mesenchyme appears than in the former experiments (Figs. 26, 27). Indeed the network of mesenchyme fills the whole explant and hardly differs from the control (Fig. 28). When the eye rudiment is surrounded by a complete mesenchyme network pigment epithelium develops in every case, as it also does in the experiments on eyes which were not

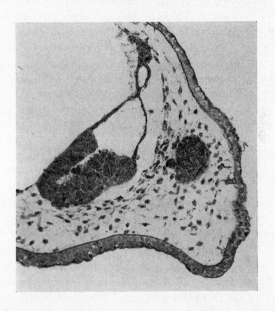

FIG. 26. Axolotl eye rudiment, separated from ectoderm and explanted with neural mesenchyme of the same age into head ectoderm. The eye is surrounded at a little distance by a thick web of mesenchyme. The pigment epithelium is slightly coloured. There are two patches of retina. The cavity of the eye contains pigment. Visual outgrowths are beginning to differentiate. Shown after 9 days explantation.

separated from the ectoderm (Table 5). In these experiments and particularly in Type C, the eye becomes larger than in the previous experiments; this is apparently connected with the density of the surrounding mesenchyme, and with the more extensive development of the barrier membranes which form from it on the surface of the eye, as well as with the larger space in explants containing only one eye instead of two and a brain.

Explants from Anterior Part of the Neural Plate without Neural Folds

In a small series of explants the anterior part of a newt neural plate, without neural folds, was used instead of the eye; the quantity of mesenchyme in these explants was also small. In seven out of eleven, large pieces of non-cupped retina linked by small pieces of pigment epithelium developed in the explants (Fig. 29), and they can be referred to Type B, Table 5. Another explant resembled Type C, and three were of Type D. Therefore the stage at which the material of the eye was taken did not exert any particular influence on the frequency of appearance of the different types when compared with the frequency in experiments from the optic vesicle stage, provided the quantity of mesenchyme in the explants was similar. We may thus compare the results of experiments on the optic vesicle stage with those which used neurula material.

Differentiation of Pigment Epithelium in the Explants

The differentiation of pigment epithelium in the explants departs considerably from that in normal control eyes. In urodeles the degree of pigmentation is always noticeably less than in the controls (Figs. 18, 21, 22, 23, 24, 26, 27), and it only appears dark grey in the most extreme cases (Figs. 20, 24). This disparity is clearly shown by comparing with the control in Fig. 28. Pigment granules never fill more than a part of the cytoplasm of the cells. In anurans the pigmentation is sometimes weak, but very often its density is no different from that in the controls (Figs. 30, 31). The thickness of the mesenchyme is very noticeable in some of these examples, so that incomplete pigmentation cannot be due to a lack of mesenchyme. It is more likely to be caused by the absence of other influences deriving from the whole embryo; this is particularly noticeable in urodele tissues, and the absence of the blood supply is probably the chief factor. Within limits pigmentation is most complete where the mesenchyme is thickest (Fig. 24); where there is less mesenchyme there is less pigmentation, and in the broken up mesenchyme network the cells of the pigment epithelium are thickened and contain hardly any pigment granules (Fig. 27b). It therefore seems likely that pigmentation is also dependent on the thickness of the surrounding mesenchyme. The nearly colourless parts of the pigment epithelium are not, strictly speaking, undeveloped: they are rather areas whose differentiation is intermediate, which have become partly retinal in character because they have been unable to accumulate pigment.

How the Formation of the Pigment Epithelium Depends on the Influence of the Mesenchyme and on the Resistance of the Walls of the Rudiments to this Influence

Once having established that the formation of the pigment epithelium depends upon the mesenchyme, we have to decide whether or not its formation in each particular part of the eye depends solely

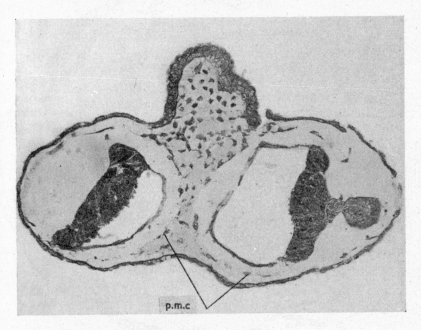

FIG. 27A. Eye rudiments of axolotl explanted with neural mesenchyme of the same age, and without separation from the head ectoderm. Web of mesenchyme surrounds the eye at a distance, and is joined to its surface by fine extracellular threads. In B (p. 48) the lens is attached to the ectoderm and to the edges of the retina by threads. p.m.c. – primary mesenchyme coat. Pigment epithelium slightly coloured. Shown 9 days after explanting.

on its being surrounded by mesenchyme. There can be no doubt that this is not so, because retina develops at many points where the

mesenchyme comes close to the eye. A comparison of the actual
position where pigment epithelium forms in different eyes shows that
the distribution is not random; it is found mainly in the apical parts
of the original fissure cavity—see Types A and B in Table 5, and

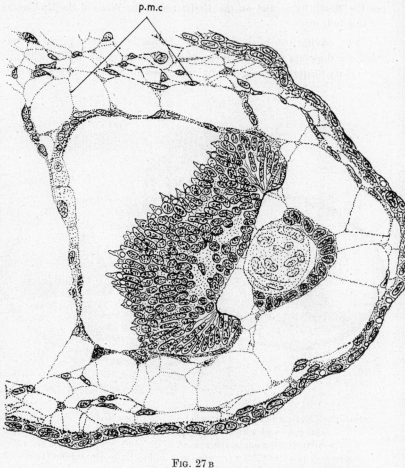

FIG. 27 B

Figs. 18 and 21—where in the absence of mesenchyme thinly drawn
out single-layered patches of retina develop. Small patches of pigment
epithelium developed on the thick walls of the retina in only two of
the axolotl experiments and three of the newt ones, and then only

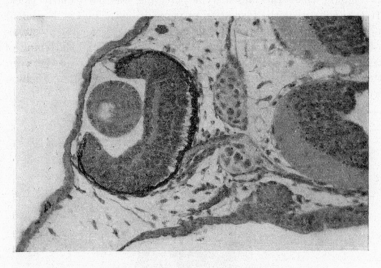

FIG. 28. Section of a normal control eye of axolotl larva, after 9 days cultivation. (Control for Figs. 20, 23, 24, 26, 27.)

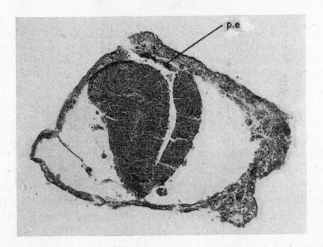

FIG. 29. The first eighth of a newt neural plate explanted in a covering of neurula ectoderm. The eye is divided into two retinas, linked by a portion of pigment epithelium. p.e. – pigment epithelium. Shown after 8 days.

in regions where the mesenchyme covering was particularly thick. It is obvious that the formation of pigment epithelium is dependent not only on the influence of the mesenchyme, but also on the resistance of the walls of the eye rudiment to the thinning and flattening of cells which is the result of this influence. It is the balance between these two factors which controls whether or not pigment epithelium will form in any particular place.

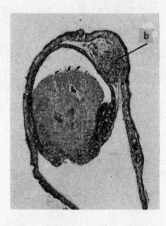

Fig. 30. Eye rudiment of *Rana arvalis* explanted in a covering of early neurula ectoderm, after 5 days explantation. The eye has developed into a mass of retina surrounded by a layer of pigment epithelium. There is a little mesenchyme lying close to the surface of the pigment epithelium. b – brain pendant.

Variation in the quantity of thick or thin patches of retina (or of pigment epithelium) in the explants is set out in Tables 5 and 6, which also show that there are consistent differences in this respect between species. In eye rudiments from newts, twenty-five out of twenty-seven developed into vesicles of retinal material, with variously shaped cavities, and different amounts of thick and thin portions, some of which turned into pigment epithelium. In axolotls, though this same type of eye predominates, pigment epithelium more often develops, and in seven out of twenty-eight cases the retinal parts lay opposite large amounts of pigment epithelium; in three cases the retina was surrounded by pigment epithelium as in normal development. *R. arvalis* is more of a borderline case. Retinal vesicles were developed in two cases, in eight cases patches of retina lay opposite large amounts of pigment epithelium, and in four cases patches of pigment epithelium flanked the retina on two sides (Fig. 31), but this arrangement was never found in urodeles. These differences correspond to the changes which occurred in the eye rudiments explanted in saline (Chapter II, section 2, and Chapter IV, section 2). In newt eye rudiments the walls are alike and in axolotls one wall is rarely thicker

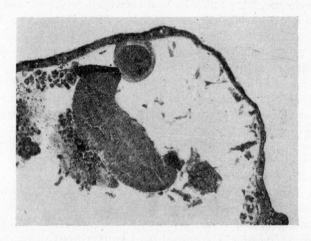

FIG. 31. Eye rudiment of *R. arvalis* enclosed in neurula ectoderm, with lateral mesoderm after 6 days explantation. The retina is cup-shaped with two patches of pigment epithelium at either end of the cup. The lens lies to one side. The retinal layers are beginning to differentiate.

than the other, while in frogs, as a rule, the difference between the two is marked (Fig. 9). In the species in which the differences between future retina and pigment epithelium are stable when the rudiments are taken from the embryo and placed in saline, one retina is usually found in the mesenchyme-epidermal vesicles; this evidently corresponds to the zone of presumptive retina in the eye rudiment. However, when these differences are still undetermined, that is in cases where all the walls of the eye are of equal thickness when cultured in saline, some thick patches alternate with thin ones in the epidermal vesicles with mesenchyme. These patches evidently develop *de novo*, and do not correspond to the arrangement of the zones in the normal formation of retina and pigment epithelium. The zones of the eye rudiment which are firmly determined to develop into thick retina are also more resistant to the influence of the mesenchyme, but the thin parts of the walls of the rudiment are easily turned into pigment epithelium under the influence of mesenchyme.

Arrangement and Differentiation of the Retinal Layers

If the explants survive long enough, the retina differentiates into the typical layers of the larval amphibian eye. Whatever the structure of the eyes may be, a lining layer of visual cells with rods and cones appears on the surface of their internal cavities (Table 5, Figs. 16, 20, 22, 23, 26, 27, 29). As in the naked explants of eye rudiments (Chapter II, section 2), a considerable number of pigment granules leave the eye rudiment through this inner surface and accumulate in the cavities up to the time at which the visual cells differentiate (Figs. 15, 16, 19, 23, 24, 26). In explants of pieces of anterior neural plate from neurulae (Chapter II, sections 3, 4, and present section), the retinal layers are arranged in exactly the same way, and are only absent where a part of the wall of the eye develops into pigment epithelium, or where this wall is very thin. The layer of visual cells does not develop on the outer surface of the urodele eye.

In *R. arvalis* the surface of the retina which is formed in the internal cavity is also covered by a layer of visual cells (Fig. 30), but where the pigment epithelium does not enclose the retina (Table 5 E, Fig. 31) the layer of visual cells is turned not into the cavity of the eye but to the internal medium of the explant. Thus in all amphibians the visual layer arises on the surface of the retina which is turned to the internal, primary cavity of the eye, but in anurans it may also arise on surfaces which are turned to the internal medium of the explant, where the original polarity of the retina is evidently still retained.

A comparison of the various experiments described in this section with the experiments using explants of eye rudiments in saline shows the effect of the composition of the medium on the differentiation of the retina. In urodeles the retinal layers never develop in saline; in anurans all except the visual layer do develop. The picture is the same in explants in ectodermal coats without mesenchyme. All the layers differentiate in the internal environment of the explants which contain mesenchyme, but in urodeles the visual layer only arises when it is in direct contact with the internal medium of the eye, which is certainly actively involved in the formation of this layer in both urodeles and anurans. The mesenchyme takes part in the creation of

TABLE 6

*Number of Thickened Retinal Patches in Eyes Explanted in
Mesenchyme-Ectoderm Coats*

No. of retinal patches in explants	Species		
	Triturus	Axolotl	*R. arvalis*
1	10	8	12
2	11	17	4
3	4	3	0
4	2	0	0

the internal environment of the explants, and is particularly important
in the formation of the boundary membranes which separate the cavity
of the eye from the internal cavity of the explant, and this cavity from
the external environment.

By way of summary, it can be said that a surrounding layer of
mesenchyme is necessary for the formation of pigment epithelium in
the eye rudiment, and that the ectomesenchyme plays a predominant
role in this; but the formation of pigment epithelium does not depend
simply on the local effect of the mesenchyme, but on a balance
between the intensity of this influence and the resistance of the eye
wall upon which it is acting. Pigmentation is never quite complete
in explants of urodele eyes and the degree of pigmentation is found
to depend on the quantity of the mesenchyme.

These experiments show that at the eye vesicle stage the future
thin or pigment epithelium and the future thick or retinal part of the
eye rudiment differ in their degree of stability from species to species:
in newts there is hardly any difference in their stability, in axolotls
these differences are faintly manifested but in *R. arvalis* the difference
is well marked. In all the species studied, the visual cell layer forms
on the internal surface of the eye cavity; but in *R. arvalis* it can also
arise on the external surface of the retina. The basic layers of the
retina differentiate in explants, and in the same way the primary
differentiation of the pigment epithelium takes place in explants which
contain mesenchyme although they lack a blood supply.

3. The Development of Eye Rudiments Grafted into Different Regions of Whole Embryos or into Embryos without Neural Plate ("Hemi-Embryos")

In order to understand more fully the nature of the conditions which affect the development of the eye rudiment and of the pigment epithelium and retinal zones within it, it is important to follow their development when they are moved into some other part of the complex which makes up the internal environment of the whole embryo. With this in view, eye rudiments at the optic vesicle stage were grafted into different regions of whole embryos or of embryos from which the neural plate and folds had been removed at the neurula stage—called later "hemi-embryos".

In structure and development these half-embryos resembled the partial embryos studied by Polezhayev (1938). The axial mesoderm usually disintegrated after the removal of the neural plate but wound-healing by the endoderm took place. The hemi-embryos had neither

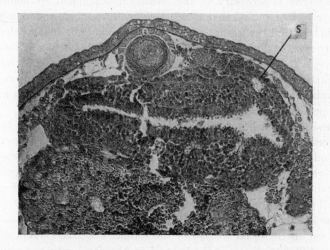

FIG. 32. Newt eye rudiment grafted into a hemi-embryo, lying in the body cavity. The eye has two thick walls of retinal material separated by an elongated fissure cavity with extensions which are lined by visual cells. The main retinal layers have differentiated. Apart from the lens seen in the photograph, a second lens is joined on to the eye and is turned towards the endoderm. Shown 10 days after explantation. S – crypts of fissure cavity.

brain, neural mesenchyme, pigment cells, or head or tail. They
enlarged and sometimes became ball-shaped as a result of an upset
in the balance between fluid intake and output, and the coelomic
cavities were noticeably enlarged. In four cases in which the wound
was covered with abdominal ectoderm the axial mesoderm was
preserved and the embryos lengthened a little — as also occurred in
the hemi-embryos described by Lopashov (1941). The yolk provided
a food supply, and the heart always developed and beat slowly.
The gills were short and unbranched, and there were no erythrocytes
in the lymph which circulated in them. It is convenient to examine
the range of behaviour of eye rudiments in embryos and hemi-embryos
together.

Newts, axolotls and the green toad *B. viridis* were used in these
experiments. The experiments involved 24 hemi-embryos, and 22 whole
embryos in which 100 eye rudiments were grafted from which the
lens-forming material had been removed. Data from grafts of eye
rudiments with lens-forming material (Chapter IV, section 4) are, as
far as necessary, also considered in this section.

When the eye rudiments were placed in the body cavity between
the somatopleur and the intestines all of them turned into retina.
Pigment epithelium did not form in the fluid environment of the body
cavity (Figs. 32–36). In such eyes, from urodeles and some anurans,

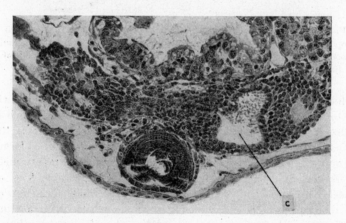

Fig. 33. Newt eye rudiment grafted into the abdominal cavity of a whole
embryo. The eye lies in the body cavity. The retinal layers are unevenly
distributed, the inner cavity of the eye is lined with visual cells and their
outgrowths; c – inner cavity of eye. Shown 13 days after operation.

5*

grafted without lens material, the cavity lay centrally, as in eyes explanted into a fluid medium, belonging to Type A, Table 5 (Figs. 32–35).

If a part of an eye perforates the lining of the body cavity and comes through to the mesenchyme, it becomes covered with pigment epithelium; this is particularly noticeable when the part which has

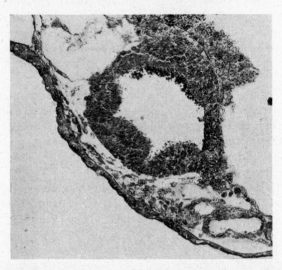

FIG. 34. Axolotl eye rudiment, grafted into hemi-embryo, 7 days after operation. A thick-walled vesicle of retinal material has formed in the body cavity; a layer of visual cells with outgrowths has developed on its inner surface; pigment has been extruded into the eye cavity.

perforated is small (Fig. 37). Similar results were obtained with newts, axolotls, green toads and in grafts of eye rudiments which included lens-forming material from other species besides. It is thus clear that in whole and hemi-embryos pigment epithelium is formed not only when thin parts of the wall of the eye rudiment are surrounded by mesenchyme, but also when other parts of the rudiment are approached by mesenchyme. The fissure cavities which form between the developing pigment epithelium and the retina are sometimes continuous with the original cavity. Pigment epithelium develops at different times in different places. The level of its development, and the amount of pigment laid down, is proportional to the extent of its separation from the retina at any one place.

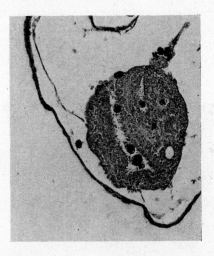

FIG. 35. Eye rudiment of *Bufo viridis* shown in the body cavity, 7 days after operation. There is a series of cavities in the eye which is developing into retina. They are lined by visual cells. Pigment has entered these cavities.

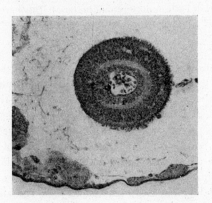

FIG. 36. Eye rudiment of *Bufo viridis*, developed into retina in the body cavity, 10 days after operation. In the middle is the cavity of the narrow invagination which juts into the retina. The layers are orientated from the cavity towards the outer surface of the eye, which is covered by a layer of visual cells, with outgrowths.

A series of eye rudiments were placed in embryos so that they were near the abdominal vein, and eight of them came to lie closely beside it. On the surface of these rudiments an atypical choroid coat with large vessels formed and in it erythrocytes could be seen. In some of the series the eye cells were bathed by blood, and these turned into

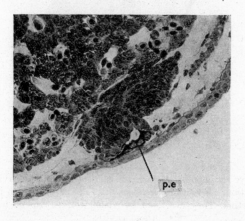

FIG. 37. Axolotl eye rudiment grafted into the abdominal region of embryo, 7 days after operation. It is lying in the body cavity and has developed almost entirely into retinal material. There are small patches of pigment epithelium (p.e.) in the subcuticular mesenchyme.

pigment epithelium (Fig. 38). In the majority of cases, in which the eye rudiments were grafted into the embryo at some distance from the large vessels, small vessels could be seen in the mesenchyme which surrounded them.

In seven experiments the eye rudiment lay between the coelomic lining and the ectoderm, i.e. in the mesenchyme of the body wall. In one of these, an axolotl, the rudiment was completely covered by pigment epithelium 14 days after operation. In other examples the eye was not completely covered, particularly on the sides nearest the epidermis and the interior organs. Retinal material was found in these, and was usually cup-shaped. Pigment epithelium never formed where the lens lay, either in these experiments or in those in which lens-forming material had been grafted with the eye (Chapter IV, section 3).

Thirteen eyes developed in the head region. When the host eye rudiments were removed and new rudiments either put in their place or near to where they had been, three of them became wholly surrounded by pigment epithelium and in the majority of the rest most of the surface was covered by pigment epithelium. The retina,

FIG. 38. Axolotl eye rudiment grafted into the vicinity of a blood vessel, 18 days after operation. An atypical choroid coat has developed over its surface. Pigment epithelium has developed in those parts of the eye which are bathed by blood.

free of pigment epithelium, lies in the area of contact with the auditory vesicle or with the host lens, turned either towards the ectoderm or rarely towards the intérior of the head. In the majority of cases it is cup-shaped (Fig. 39), sometimes with a narrow opening. As before, where lenses were formed, whether from normal lens-forming ectoderm or from the eye, pigment epithelium was absent from the area occupied by them.

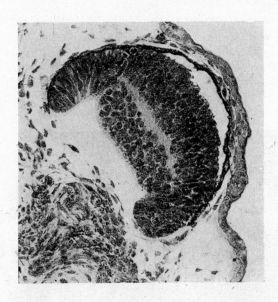

FIG. 39. Axolotl eye rudiment, grafted into head region of embryo, shown 6 days after operation. Pigment epithelium has developed where the eye is in contact with the sub-cuticular mesenchyme. There is a marked difference between the surface of the retina which is differentiated into layers, and the undifferentiated iris region.

Extent of Pigment Epithelium Formation and Degree of Pigmentation

Table 7 shows the distribution of eyes with different amounts of pigment epithelium in the experiments on whole urodele embryos. From this table and from a comparison of the quantity of pigment epithelium which develops in the different experimental conditions, it seems clear that its formation is dependent upon the eyes being surrounded by a mesenchyme layer; it never arises in the fluid environment of the body cavity. In one case the eye rudiment lay inside the endoderm, and here pigment epithelium arose only beside brain tissue, where a piece of the eye was covered with mesenchyme derived from the grafted rudiment itself. A thin vessel grew out over the surface of the pigment epithelium at this point. In the hemi-embryos, and even more in the whole embryos, there was not only more mesenchyme than in the explants, but it closely invested the grafted eye rudiment, and in contrast to what was observed in the explants, pigment epithelium differentiated from all areas of the eye rudiment.

In a series starting with grafts made into the subcutaneous area of hemi-embryos, then into the subcutaneous body region of whole embryos, and ending with those in the head region of embryos, the increase in the quantity of mesenchyme is attended by an increase in the quantity of pigment epithelium, until in some cases it entirely surrounds the eye rudiment.

TABLE 7

How the Position of Grafted Urodele Eye Rudiments in the Embryo Affects their Development

Position of grafted eye	Eyes consisting of pure retina	Eyes consisting of both pigment epithelium and retina		Eye composed of retina, the whole surrounded by pigment epithelium
		Pigment epithelium covered by mesenchyme	Pigment epithelium clearly covered by choroid coat	
In body cavity	7 (axol.) 4 (newt)	–	–	–
Partly in body cavity, partly outside it	–	9 (axol.)	6 (axol.) 2 (newt)	–
In subcutaneous layer of body	–	3 (axol.) 1 (newt)	1 (axol.) 1 (newt)	1 (axol.)
In head beside host eye	–	8 (axol.) 2 (newt)	–	–
In head, host eye removed	–	–	–	3 (axol.)

Full pigmentation is achieved in urodele rudiments which are vascularized, a condition which cannot, of course, be satisfied in explants. Indeed eye cells can turn into pigment epithelium if they are brought into direct contact with large blood vessels. When the cells come into contact with blood, which is more physiologically active than the lymphoid internal environment of explants a second stage of pigmentation is attained. This is never seen in explants.

Zones in the Embryonic Eye which are Resistant to the Influence of the Mesenchyme

As in experiments with explants, these experiments also showed that some parts of the eye rudiment were more resistant to the influence of the mesenchyme than others. Usually one of these regions is particularly resistant, and does not become covered with pigment epithelium: this is the place where the lens is forming from the ecto- derm, or from other lens-forming material. However, the experiments on axolotls (in which the lens is not formed from the ectoderm) demon- strate that these regions can also exist independently of the formation of the lens. Out of sixteen axolotl eyes lying in mesenchyme — some with two retinas each — four were surrounded by pigment epithelium. Twelve of the retinas were more or less cup shaped. Of the twelve, one was turned towards an auditory vesicle, another to the lens of the

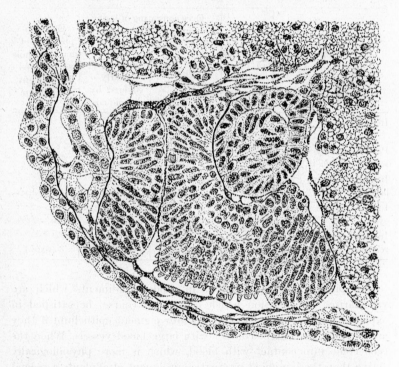

FIG. 40. Axolotl eye rudiment, with portions of lens ectoderm, grafted into hemi-embryos, 7 days after explantation. Two retinas have developed; the larger is attached to the lens and the smaller to the kidney tubules. The large retina has differentiated into layers in the thickest parts and has begun to separate from the lens. The small retina is undifferentiated, and is made up of columnar cells; many mitoses are found in its external layer. An inner cornea anlage lies around the lens and the margin of the retina.

host, six were turned towards the ectoderm, one to the endoderm, and three to the inside of the head. It is obvious that one of the walls of the eye is more predisposed to turn into retina. Particularly when an appropriate substrate is available, a polarized and approximately normal eye develops with a cup-shaped retina. Two of the eyes resembled those which developed in the body cavity. In these eyes, the fissure cavity lay between the two thick walls and pigment epithelium separated from one of them; the envelopment by mesenchyme obviously did not coincide with the primary polarity of the rudiment, and pigment epithelium therefore developed at the surface of the presumptive retina.

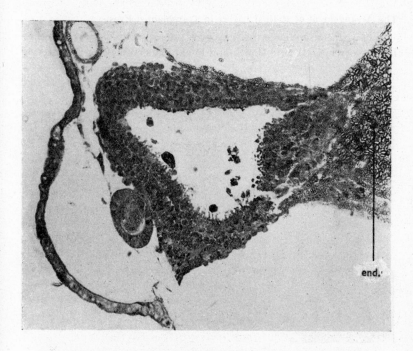

FIG. 41. Axolotl eye rudiment, grafted with a piece of lens ectoderm into hemi-embryo. It was attached to the ectoderm and endoderm and by being stretched between them lost its cup-shape. The retina is differentiated into layers with visual outgrowths, facing towards the eye cavity, which contains extruded pigment. A film of mesenchyme lies over the lens—the future internal cornea. There is no pigment epithelium. end – endoderm.

If the stable retinal area is normally formed and develops into a cup shape, the mesenchyme will not extend to the bottom of the invagination whether or not a lens is present. The developing inner cornea, which is a continuation of the mesenchyme coats of the eye (Figs. 40, 41), stretches across the opening of the eye cup without entering its invagination. In anurans mesoderm cells do enter the invagination, where they form the vessels of the hyaloid blood supply, and this also occurs in the invaginations of eye cups in grafted eyes (Figs. 36, 42, 62, 63). These vessels appear after the surface of the rudiment has been covered with mesenchyme. The development of the cup shape by the eye assists its inner wall to turn into retina by preventing the mesenchyme from approaching it.

The Arrangement of Retinal Layers in Transplanted Eyes

When grafts are made into embryos the arrangement of the retinal layers corresponds with that found in explants. Wherever the internal

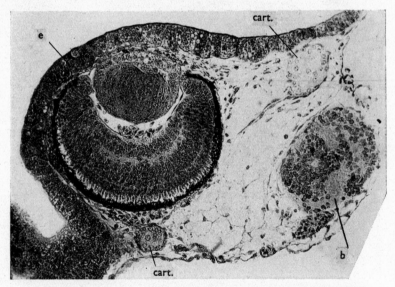

FIG. 42. Eye rudiment of *Pelobates* grafted with lens material into an embryo, 6 days after operation. The eye lies in a mesenchyme islet on the surface of the endoderm to which the lens adheres. The eye is typical, all the layers are present in the retina, and the pigment epithelium is surrounded by a choroid coat which contains erythrocytes. There are hyaloid vessels between the lens and retina. There are two small pieces of cartilage near the endoderm. b – brain pendant, cart. – cartilage, e – endoderm.

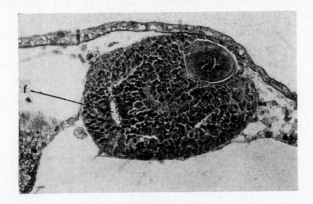

FIG. 43. Newt eye rudiment grafted into hemi-embryo, 7 days after grafting. The thicker, cup-shaped wall of retinal material, which has begun to differentiate into its basic layers, is grasped by a thinner wall of undifferentiated retina; the fissure cavity (f) lies between these walls.

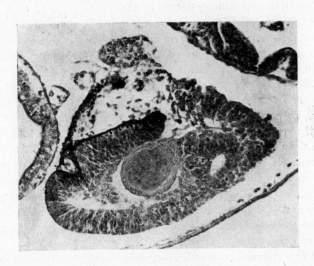

FIG. 44. Eye rudiment of *R. arvalis* grafted into body cavity of an embryo. A part of its surface is covered by mesenchyme. Pigment epithelium arises on the surface of the eye linked to the mesenchyme, and grows over the surface of the mesentery. The retina is hyper cup-shaped--its edges almost meet. Shown 6 days after operation.

cavity appears in the eye rudiment, it is covered by a layer of visual cells, with outgrowths (Figs. 32, 33, 35, 41, 43, 44), but these cells are absent from that surface of the urodele eye which is turned towards the body cavity. In anurans, however, the visual cells may also form on the outer surface of the rudiment. Fig. 36 shows an eye rudiment of *B. viridis* developing in a body cavity; the retinal layers of cells are orientated between the outer surface of the eye and the deep invagination which lies centrally.

Pigment granules pass through the surface of the eye on which visual cells will later be formed, just as they do in the explants (Figs. 32, 34, 35, 40, 41 and also 46 and 58), and wherever a cavity is found in the eye, however insignificant it may be, large numbers of mitoses are invariably found in the cells beside it. They occur in urodeles from about 4–6 days after grafting and continue until the retina segregates into layers; at this time in normal eyes mitotic figures are most numerous in the external layer of the retina (Fig. 45); they are not found throughout the whole thickness of the retina. This suggests that the conditions at the surface of the retina favour the formation and differentiation of the visual layer of cells.

The growth of the eye rudiment depends upon its supply of nutrients. In point of size the series starts with the smallest explants grown in saline, and continues with explants in ectoderm-mesenchyme coats, then proceeds via eye rudiments in hemi-embryos to end with the largest rudiments which are those grown in whole embryos. Much depends upon the degree of vascularization of these grafts. In addition, the layer of visual cells grows more rapidly than the rest. This can be seen in eye rudiments in the body cavity which develop entirely into retina. Their visual layers often become thrown into folds (Fig. 32) and sometimes the fusion of the primary and secondary cavities so formed results in an eye of very complicated appearance. It is only when the retina succeeds in becoming cup-shaped and is opposed by the pigment epithelium which does not prevent the retina from rolling up, that the growth of the visual cell layer can assist the development of a normal shaped eye.

The experiments on grafting eye rudiments into different regions of embryos confirm and extend earlier findings. The formation of pigment epithelium depends upon the eye rudiments being surrounded by mesenchyme. The larger the area covered, the greater is the quantity of pigment epithelium. It is also dependent on the blood supply, and in urodeles full pigmentation is reached only when

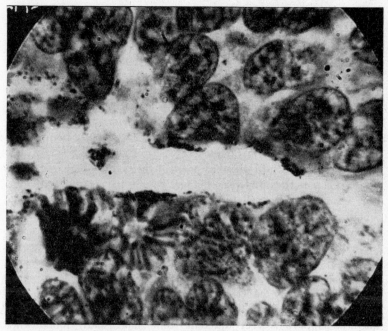

FIG. 45. Part of fissure cavity in retina which has developed from
a grafted axolotl eye. There are many mitoses along the surface of the
fissure, and pigment granules are entering the cavity. Shown 6 days
after grafting.

a blood supply is available. Although pigment epithelium can
develop from any part of the eye rudiment if large quantities of mesenchyme are lying sufficiently close, resistance to the influence of the
mesenchyme varies in different areas. Contact with a substrate assists
an area to stabilize, as the lens, for example, helps by protecting the
retina from the influence of the mesenchyme. The regularities of
layer arrangement under the experimental condition described may
now be summarized as follows: all the eye cavities are lined with a layer
of visual cells, but in anurans this layer may also appear on the outer
surface of the eye, which develops only into retina. The appearance of
the visual cell layer at the surface of the primary eye cavity is preceded by the extrusion of pigment granules into this cavity, and by
mitotic activity in the surface layer. It seems likely then that conditions at the surface layer of the retina are important for its mitotic
activity and differentiation.

4. Behaviour of Eye Rudiments Grafted into Different Regions of Whole Embryos following Preliminary Explantation

Two further questions remained to be answered. Firstly, how will the eye rudiment develop if ectomesenchyme is not included in its environment, and secondly, can rudiments after explantation into saline develop pigment epithelium? In order to answer these questions, eye rudiments without lens-forming material from fourteen newts, fifteen axolotls, nineteen *R. arvalis* and nine *B. viridis* were placed in saline as described in Chapter II, section 2; after 2–3 days they were transplanted into different parts of the body of embryos of the same species at the optic vesicle stage. During the period of explantation ectomesenchyme cells emerged from them, and the brain became separated off. In the evaluation of the results reported here, data on grafts including lens-forming material have also been considered; some of these rudiments were taken from *R. ridibunda* (Chapter IV, section 4). The results in different series are not fully comparable, because the experiments were set up at room temperature, which varied considerably with the time of year.

The state of the eye rudiments at the moment when they are grafted into the embryo is very different from that usually found when rudiments are grafted at the optic vesicle stage. As was clearly shown in Chapter II, section 2 (Figs. 5, 6, 7), within 2 days the eye rudiments collapse, the cavity becomes fissure like or lost, and the walls thicken. In anurans, but not in urodeles, nuclear and reticular layers not infrequently begin to differentiate within 3 days. In control urodele larvae, the walls of the eye cup become unevenly thickened after 48 hours, the lens placode thickens and pigmentation sometimes begins. In control anurans of the same age there is a sharp difference in the thickness of the layers, the pigment epithelium has begun to darken, and the lens to separate from the ectoderm, but the retina is still not differentiated into layers.

The differentiation in the eye rudiments which had undergone preliminary explantation in saline if placed in the body cavity (twenty-eight cases) never varied in any important particular from the development of eyes which were grafted directly into the body cavity (Chapter III, section 3) (Fig. 46). These eye rudiments which had been in saline for 3 days and then found themselves surrounded by mesenchyme never developed pigment epithelium, no matter how thick the mesenchyme was, but remained as a mass

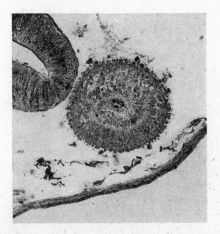

FIG. 46. Eye rudiment of *Rana arvalis*, grafted into an embryo after 2 days explantation. It lies in the body cavity and has developed entirely into retina. In the middle are the remains of the invagination cavity, towards which the retinal layers are orientated; on the outer surface of the retina are visual cells with outgrowths.

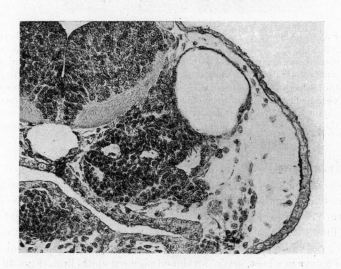

FIG. 47. Newt eye rudiment 8 days after grafting into an embryo following a preliminary explantation period of 3 days. The explant lies in the posterior part of the head. No pigment epithelium has developed. The small cavities inside the eye are lined by visual cells with outgrowths.

of retina, with internal cavities (Fig. 47), and without lenses in spite
of contact with the ectoderm of the host.

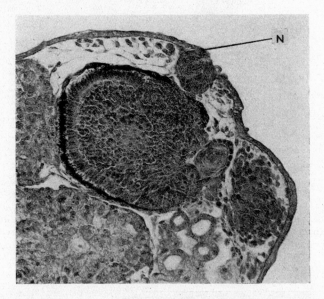

Fig. 48. Newt eye rudiment, 7 days after grafting into an embryo,
following a preliminary explantation period of 2 days. In the area of
contact between eye and ectoderm, a lens has developed and an invagination opposite it, in the retina. Pigment epithelium has developed from
the surface of the grafted eye, and under it is a well developed layer of
visual cells, with outgrowths. Pigment epithelium is covered by the mesenchyme coat. A nasal placode has developed from the ectoderm near
the eye, and the adjoining pigment epithelium is poorly developed.
N – nasal placode.

Those grafts, explanted for 48 hours and then transplanted into
mesenchyme gave completely different results. Eight out of ten newt
eyes lying in mesenchyme evoked the formation of a lens in the ectoderm, became cup-shaped themselves, and developed pigment epithelium over their outer surface (Fig. 48). In axolotls, in eight out of
ten eyes without lenses which had lived 2 days explanted, and then
6 or 8 days in a host, seven developed pigment epithelium (Figs. 49, 50).
In seven out of eight eyes which had lens-ectoderm, pigment epithelium
was formed (Fig. 51), but sometimes only a small part of the eye was
covered by it (Fig. 52). This happened when part of the eye entered

the body cavity. In a few cases it is easy to see that (Figs. 48, 54) the layer of cells which lies beneath the pigment epithelium develops into visual cells. In the anuran *R. arvalis* pigment epithelium developed in three out of five cases (Fig. 53); in one of them, developing in mesenchyme, there were no visual outgrowths on the surface although its lens lay in the centre, while similar eyes developing

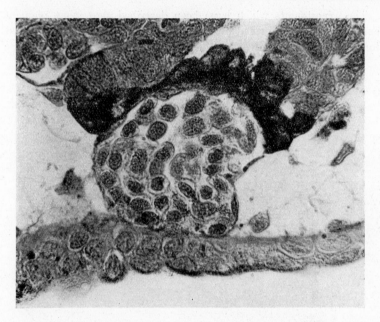

FIG. 49. Axolotl eye rudiment, 8 days after grafting into body cavity of an embryo, following 2 days explantation. Wherever large blood vessels run over the eye, pigment epithelium with tall cells has developed.

in the body cavity always formed a layer of visual cells on their surface (Fig. 46). Pigment epithelium also developed in two lens carrying eye rudiments of *Rana ridibunda* (Fig. 54) and in a single case of *Bufo viridis* grafted after previous explantation with lens-forming ectoderm. When newt (Fig. 48) or axolotl eyes came in contact with ectoderm, nasal placodes developed in three cases.

Cartilage is never found in eyes grafted after a preliminary period of life as explants, although it is often formed near directly grafted ones in anurans (Chapter IV, section 4). This is an indication that the

6*

former grafts do not contain free ectomesenchyme, it having separated
from them in culture. It follows that such ectomesenchyme is not
available for the formation of the coats of eyes grafted back into
embryos after some time in culture.

Reconstruction of the Eyes after Delayed Grafting; the Time of Differentiation and Degree of Pigmentation in Pigment Epithelium

The experiments which have been described show that pigment
epithelium can be formed even in eyes which have been explanted
for 2 days before grafting. Other reorganizations are also possible

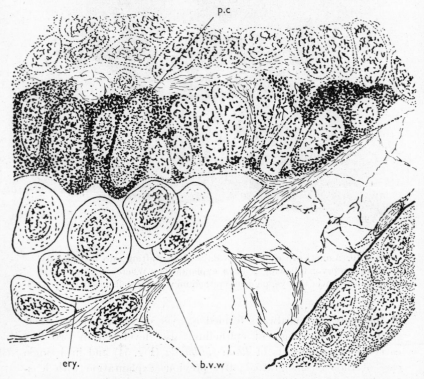

Fig. 50. Axolotl eye rudiment explanted for 2 days and then grafted
into an embryo, in which its surface was crossed by a large vessel,
and its cells were directly bathed by blood. These cells are unflattened,
but have begun to accumulate pigment. p.c. – cells which are accumulating pigment, ery – erythrocytes, b.v.w. – wall of blood vessel.
Drawn 5 days after grafting.

in these eyes: thus cells which lie under the pigment epithelium can develop into a layer of visual cells, and when the retina evokes the formation of a new lens, the whole retina acquires a new polarity which conforms to the position of the lens. All these phenomena are

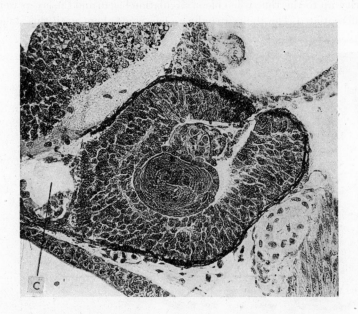

FIG. 51. Axolotl eye rudiment with a piece of lens-ectoderm at the apex, explanted for 2 days and then grafted into the posterior head region of an embryo. The eye is hyper-cup-shaped, and the retina surrounds the lens and an ectodermal pendant. The eye is covered with pigment epithelium, which has developed wherever the vascularized mesenchyme coat covers it, except where the eye rests against the chorda. c – chorda.
Shown 8 days after grafting.

observed only in eye rudiments which are grafted 2 days after explantation. After the second 24-hour period, the retina normally achieves a considerable thickness, and the pigment epithelium is partially darkened, but there has still been no formation of layers in the retina. After 3 days all the layers in the retina have differentiated. Explanted eyes are thus able to regulate up to the point at which the eye differentiates into layers. These results confirm those obtained by Dragomirov (1935b) which showed that the retina of the common newt can produce pigment epithelium up to the stage at which the external gills appear and the blood starts to circulate. They also correspond to Eakin's (1947) results in which inversion of embryonic and larval retinas of the Californian tree frog, *Hyla regilla*, resulted in a change of polarity up to the time when blood circulation began and the layers were differentiated. The ability to induce a lens is also kept until this stage.

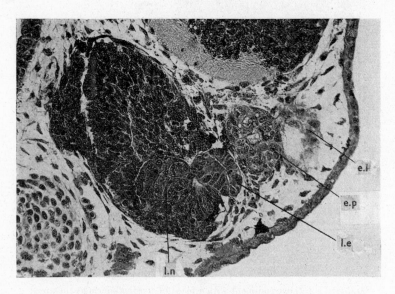

FIG. 52. Axolotl eye rudiment with a piece of lens-ectoderm at the apex, explanted for 2 days, and then grafted into an embryo. It has developed into retina, and the ectodermal pendant has formed a chain, which joins the retina to the ectoderm as follows: the lens nucleus (which is embedded in the retina)—lens epithelium—epidermal pendant. e.i. – epidermal invagination, e.p. – epidermal pendant, l.e. – lens epithelium, l.n. – lens nucleus. Shown 6 days after grafting.

Like other rudiments, the eye goes through some parts of its development when it is explanted, but the differentiation of pigment epithelium is retarded compared with that of control eyes or of the host. When the pigment epithelium of the transplant is pale grey, that of the host is fully pigmented, although it is 2 days younger. Differentiation in the layer of visual cells which arises under the pigment epithelium is also correspondingly delayed. Thus it would appear that the development of eye cells is markedly retarded by a change in the course of their development, and it is obvious that in the eye rudiment the period during which the cell differentiation occurs can depend a great deal upon environmental conditions. In gastrula ectoderm, on the other hand, similar variations do not produce changes in the period during which the neighbouring parts can exert their influence and usually decide the course of its differentiation (Holtfreter, 1938a; Gallera, 1952, 1953).

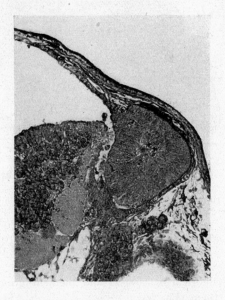

FIG. 53. *Rana arvalis* eye rudiment, grafted into head region of an embryo after 2 days explantation, shown 4 days after grafting. Unevenly pigmented pigment epithelium has differentiated from the surface covered by mesenchyme. The remains of the invagination cavity lies in the centre of the retina.

Differences in Formation of Pigment Epithelium, and their Importance in Understanding the Basic Mechanisms of its Development

Some of the eyes which had been explanted before grafting lay in the region of the abdominal blood vessels. Fixed preparations, taken at different periods, showed how pigment epithelium is formed when the eye is directly bathed by blood. Under these conditions, the formation of pigment epithelium does not start with the flattening and spreading out of its cells over a mesenchyme film. Instead, the

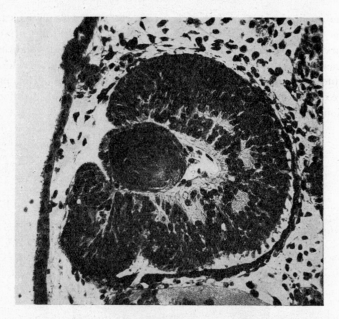

FIG. 54. Eye rudiment of *Rana ridibunda*, with lens forming material, explanted for 2 days and then grafted into an embryo, shown 8 days after grafting. Pigment epithelium has developed from the surface of the eye; the cell layer lying under it has formed visual cells. A small placode has developed in the ectoderm at the edge of the eye cup.

cells remain cylindrical or cubical and pigment granules begin to accumulate in them (Fig. 50).

Pigmentation of eye cells is thus brought about in different ways, and this fact makes it possible to discover some of the causal relations which lead to pigmentation. When the rudiment is surrounded by a mesenchyme film and the cells spread out over it, pigment epithelium develops, but in urodeles this alone does not lead to complete pigmentation. In them the basic factor responsible for pigmentation is the close relation between the cells of the separating outer layer of the eye and the internal fluid environment of the developing explant. Direct bathing by the blood stream is even more effective, because the blood is a better vehicle for oxygen and nutrients than the lymphoid environment of the explant. Pigmentation is evoked, in the absence of flattening of the cells, if only one of their ends is bathed by blood, and pigmentation can only become complete if blood is present. These courses of pigment formation differ only in their intensity. The blood completes a process which can be begun without its participation.

The experiments on grafts of eyes explanted before grafting show that up to the onset of the circulation of the blood and the differentiation of layers in the retinas of control embryos, such eyes can differentiate pigment epithelium from the surface layer, convert the layer which lies beneath it to visual cells, reverse their polarity and induce lenses. Stratification of the retina takes place much later than in the controls. These experiments, with those described in previous sections, show that pigmentation of the epithelium can take place both when the eyes are surrounded by mesenchyme, and when the surface of the eye is directly bathed with blood; full pigmentation of the cells is achieved only under the influence of blood.

5. The Development of the Eye Rudiment in Isolated Heads and in Embryos without Blood

If blood is so important for the nourishment and growth of the eye, and for the differentiation of the pigment epithelium—which in urodeles cannot be completed without it—then how does the pigment epithelium develop in the head of an embryo deprived of blood? To what extent is it pigmented? Does the normal choroid coat develop in the absence of blood? Two types of experiment were set up to provide answers to these questions. In the first, isolated heads of twenty-four axolotls, eighteen *R. arvalis* and eighteen *R. esculenta* at the optic vesicle stage were cultured in saline; the developing endoderm was removed from a part of such heads. In the second, the blood anlage was removed from beneath the ectoderm of twenty late *R. esculenta* neurulae. The two sets differed in that the isolated frog and axolotl heads lived up to 14 days, in a normal condition, while the larvae were viable for only 7 days, after which they were fixed.

The heads, and particularly anuran heads with endoderm intact, enlarged if they were completely enclosed in ectoderm. In *R. arvalis* the shape of the eye was atypical and elongated. External inspection of the isolated axolotl heads showed that the pigmentation of the iris was poor and unequally distributed, in the form of dark spots at its margin. In controls of this age (9–14 days) the iris is already completely pigmented.

The pigment epithelium in isolated axolotl heads, as in explanted eye rudiments, is never saturated with pigment granules. When the explanted head is much swollen the mesenchyme net lies, as in explants, at some distance from the pigment epithelium and is connected to it by threads emerging from the net and by separate cells (Fig. 55).

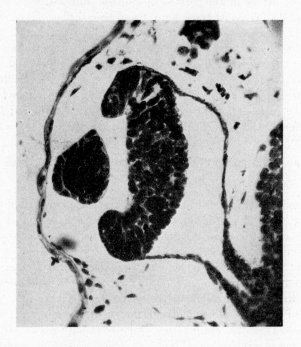

FIG. 55. Structure of an axolotl eye, developing in an isolated embryonic head. The pigment epithelium is only slightly darkened; the mesenchyme net does not lie closely to it, and there are no vessels.

In the more compact head explants the mesenchyme net comes somewhat closer to the pigment epithelium and this is then darker. Vessels never arose between the pigment epithelium and the mesenchyme layer whether the distance between them was large or small. In the compact explants the lenses lay close to the invagination of the retina; there is only a slight cavity, and the iris, though well developed in the controls, is almost absent in these eyes.

In the explanted frog heads, in contrast to the axolotl, a large part of the surface of the external layer of the eye becomes just as darkly pigmented as in controls. In the pond frog, *R. esculenta*, lenses became separated from the ectoderm in every case, and being pressed closely to the bottom of the retina they were covered from outside by the inner cornea. In the sharp-nosed frog, *R. arvalis*, the lenses in the explanted heads did not lose their connexion with the ecto-

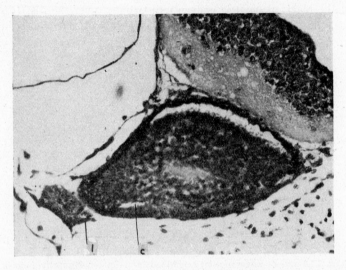

FIG. 56. Structure of *Rana arvalis* eye, developing in isolated embryonic head. The lens has kept its connexion with the ectoderm. The cavity of the elongated eye is closed, and visual cells have developed on its surface. l — lens, c — cavity of the eye.

derm, and this led to alterations in their shape, and to a pulling away of one end of the retina with the lens. The invagination is lost, and only a narrow fissure remains, which may either disappear completely or become enclosed in the retina; then the surface of the iris, on the side of this fissure cavity, becomes covered with visual outgrowths (Fig. 56). The cupped shape of the eye is usually lost. The inner cornea is stretched from the mesenchyme coat of the eye to the point where the lens is attached to the ectoderm.

The mesenchyme either forms a thin net around these eyes, similar to that found in axolotls, or it forms a thin film close to the pigment epithelium, which continues into the inner cornea (Fig. 56). As in axolotls, no vessels ever form between this mesenchyme coat and the pigment epithelium. In cases in which the cup shape of the retina was kept, cells entered the invagination and formed the vessels of the hyaloid blood system.

The results from the experiments which removed the blood forming anlage are not basically very different. Seven days after operation, the diameter of the larval eye is only about 0·7 that of the controls, and the black pigment is unevenly distributed over the iris. In sections, the mesenchyme coat of these eyes appears, like those found

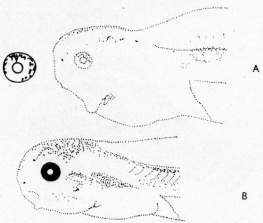

FIG. 57 A and B. Effect of removing blood anlage on development of eye of *Rana esculenta*. A — operated embryo 7 days after operation; left — the isolated eye, B — control embryo, C — eye of operated embryo, D — eye of control embryo. Pigment has accumulated unevenly in the pigment epithelium of the experimental eye; the iris is undeveloped, and the mesenchyme coat consists of a thin film of cells without vessels in it.

in isolated eyes, as a thin net which passes into the inner cornea where it covers the front of the eye. The lens separates from the ectoderm and enters the invagination of the retina, and the iris does not develop. There are no vessels in the mesenchyme coat, but the vessels of the hyaloid blood supply are present in the invagination of the eye. Pigment is often irregularly distributed in the pigment epithelium, and the epithelium is thickened where pigment accumulates (Fig. 57). Pigment granules are extruded from these thickened cells (Lopashov, 1951).

Jolly (1944) investigated the origin of the vessels of the eye in isolated embryonic amphibian heads from which the blood anlage had been removed. As in our experiments, the hyaloid vessels alone were developed. Vessels do not arise in the choroid coat when blood is absent, and the coat retains a resemblance to the ectomesenchyme coats described in the previous section.

Knower (1907) and Kemp (1953) studied the changes in the shape of the eye of *R. pipiens* embryos from which the already functioning heart rudiment had been removed, and Kemp and Quinn (1954) also

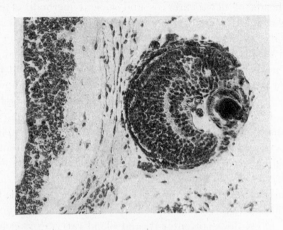

Fig. 57 c

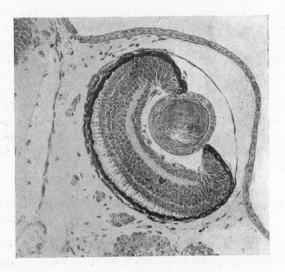

Fig. 57 d

made a similar series of studies on bloodless embryos, using *Ambly-stoma punctatum*. They too found that the eye cavity did not develop, and though vessels were found in the eye coats, this was probably because their operations were carried out on older rudiments than ours. Walder (1950) in a detailed examination of the effect of dis-rupting the blood supply on the origin of microphthalmia, used isolated heads of newt embryos and several methods of excluding the circulation. He found tha tmicrophthalmia always occurred and that its severity depended upon the time and effectiveness of stopping the blood supply. When the blood was completely excluded from the isolated heads the eye pigmentation was incomplete and irregular, and this was also the case when the heart anlage was removed, as in the above described experiments with isolated axolotl heads. However, absence of histological analysis prevented Walder from reaching conclusions about the dependence of pigmentation on the circulation of the blood, or from explaining the importance of the circulation for the development of the vessels in the mesenchyme coat of the eye.

All these results do however show that without a blood supply the eye can only accomplish the first period of its development. Only the primary mesenchyme coat, derived from the ectomesenchyme, deve-lops. The blood does not enter it, and blood-carrying vessels are not formed. The eye acquires the primary cup shape, and there is no definite iris or large cavity; these develop only with the onset of the circulation. This may be both because the retina does not grow with-out a blood supply and because there is no internal pressure in the eye. Pigmentation is limited in the urodele eye, while in anurans pigmentation is complete if only one mesenchyme coat is present; this illustrates anew the difference in the dependence of the urodele and anuran eye on environmental conditions. Just as the anuran retina differentiates further than the urodele in saline, so anuran pigmentation can be complete when there is only a single mesenchyme coat, while urodeles require the influence of the blood to achieve the same result.

6. The Importance of the Mesenchyme Coat and the Blood Supply in the Normal Development of the Eye Rudiments

Observations on living material and comparison with histological preparations were added to results from these experiments when it was sought to assess the importance of experimentally discovered regularities for normal development. Axolotls, *R. esculenta*, *R. arvalis* and *Pelobates* were all used, and newts and *Bufo viridis* provided material for a separate series of observations. Tables 8–9 give a summary of the results from axolotls and *Pelobates*.

The details of development vary from species to species, but this is not taken into account in classifying development into numerical stages. Thus muscle contraction, which is the most important criterion for Stage 18 in anurans (Rugh, 1948), occurs in the majority of species when the fins are well formed and when the tail bud begins to look like a tail, but in *Bufo viridis* the contractions start before the fins have been formed. In frogs, toads and other anurans the fins develop a considerable time after the formation of the tail bud, but in *Pelobates* the two develop simultaneously. Since variations between species constitute an important aspect of the present work, the comparison of the stages of development is made relative to the development of the optic rudiment.

Formation of the Mesenchyme Coats and Changes in the Connexions between them and the Eye

In axolotls (Table 8) at Stage 21–22 when the neural tube is closing (Table 8a), only isolated mesenchyme cells lie around the optic vesicle. Later on, at Stage 24–25 when there are 6–8 somites, the eye is surrounded by mesenchyme, but the connexions between the eye and the mesenchyme are slight, and between the eye and the ectoderm are almost non-existent. This is the stage during which the cells of the ectomesenchyme emerge from the neural crest on either side of the head (Stone, 1922; Raven, 1931; Hörstadius, 1950). Mesenchyme does not invade the area of contact between eye and ectoderm.

Until the start of the circulation (Table 8, b–g), the mesenchyme cells keep some sort of attachment to the eye at separate points. Sections show that they lie tangentially to the surface of the eye, and pass inwards to it only occasionally, uniting with the surface in most places by extra-cellular threads. The anterior pole is, as earlier, inaccessible to the mesenchyme, and when the eye is separated from the ectoderm, a clearly outlined transparent spot, quite free of mesenchyme, remains on the ectoderm at the point of its former contact with the eye (Table 8, d).

At the stage when the heart has begun to beat and the gills are becoming cone-like (Stage 36, Table 8, g), the thick flat mesenchyme coat which surrounds the eye can be seen quite clearly in the living eye. It now begins to penetrate between the eye and the ectoderm. In the following stage (Stage 37, Table 8, h) the blood can be seen moving, and if the coat is cut, pinkish erythroblasts emerge. The coat lies close to the eye, and is firmly attached to it. At this stage vessel-forming cells appear under the primary mesenchyme coat, and the vessels begin to form at the posterior pole. At first the blood follows many paths beneath the coat, the pattern differing from embryo to embryo; regular routes are only established as the vessels are laid down.

In anurans (*Pelobates* and *Rana*) the formation of the mesenchyme coat is basically similar, but the optic vesicle is surrounded by mesenchyme by the early tail bud stage, — in *Pelobates* the layer is particularly thick—because in anurans the ectomesenchyme starts to creep under the ectoderm already during neurulation (Stone, 1929; Ichikawa, 1937). As in axolotls, the mesenchyme cells lie apart from the eye for a long time and are only linked to its surface by fine threads. Later, when the retina has invaginated, these cells become closely united to each other, but at first they are only loosely attached to the eye, and the coat can be easily removed. The pigment epithelium is attached to this coat by thin threads, and mesenchyme cells lie sparsely scattered on its surface. By Stage 20 (Table 9, c) the coat is formed, and surrounds the eye up to the point of attachment of the lens to the ectoderm, which is about to rupture. At this time, those mesenchyme cells which form the vessels and the erythroblasts appear between the mesenchyme coat and the pigment epithelium. Simultaneously they enter the eye fissure and the incipient cavity between the retina and the lens. The hyaloid blood system is built up here by the vessel-forming cells. Observations on living material show that the attachments between the mesenchyme coat and the eye develop rapidly after blood enters the coat and that the mesodermal cells apparently fasten the primary ectomesenchyme coat to the eye. After the start of the circulation the lens separates from the ectoderm, the inner cornea forms, and the eye becomes enclosed by a continuous mesenchyme coat (Table 9, d).

The comparison of observations and dissections on living embryos with the results of experiments reveal their profound agreemet. The eye is surrounded primarily by a continuous mesenchyme coat but remains apart from it for quite a long period. The relationship between the coat and the eye is difficult to make out in the normal eye, because the two are so tightly pressed together. It is best understood by investigating the relationship in the enlarged eyes in explants containing only neural mesenchyme. The neural crest is the source of the mesenchyme coat in amphibians, but even if ectomesenchyme cells normally come from the eye rudiment itself, the secannot play a very large part in the building of the coat, least of all in urodeles. In fact large amounts of mesenchyme are found only in explants in which other sources of neural mesenchyme have been included. The mesodermal vessel-forming cells enter loops in the primary coat through which blood cells circulate before the narrower vessels begin to form. The coat then comes to lie close to the eye, and becomes attached to it, probably by the mesodermal cells of the vessels.

Mechanical Systems in the Development of the Eye

At the optic vesicle stage the relationship between the internal pressure of the eye and the restriction of space produced by the stretched ectoderm plays an important part in the formation of the eye (Chapter II); unless the eye rudiment is confined—this is particularly the case in urodeles—it enlarges and develops pigment epithelium. But at this stage, while the eye rudiment has a relatively dense consistency, it does not swell when placed in Holtfreter solution, but merely shrinks at the expense of its cavity.

The situation changes from the moment the mesenchyme coats are formed and the circulation starts; the coats form a closed system around the eye, and are quite strong. If the eye is slit through its posterior wall, the coats and the pigment epithelium immediately stretch and turn inside out as the tension is released. The actual consistency of the retina alters noticeably at this period, and it begins to swell if placed in Holtfreter solution; in tadpoles this swelling will occur at even later stages. It is obvious that the size and shape of the eye already depend on the balance between the internal pressure and the restricting mesenchyme coat. Coulombre (1956) showed in chicks how the retina, which has no supporting function of its own, begins to build up an internal pressure in the eye cavity from the onset of blood circulation. In this way changes in the mechanical forces shape the eye during its development, though systems which shape the eye are not restricted to these mechanisms (see Chapter IV).

Origin and Development of Pigmentation of the Eye

In urodeles two periods in the development of the pigmentation can be clearly seen. Until the beginning of the invagination of the retina, the original pigment of the embryo, in species with dark eggs, is in the form of granules within the eye cells. It is widely distributed in the retina and the zone of the presumptive iris, although there is none at the bottom of the eye invagination which has a light yellowish colour. At the stage when the retina is a flattened cup shape, and when the lens placode begins to thicken, new pigment begins to arise in both retinal and pigment epithelium cells, close to their apposed surfaces, and it is found also in the remains of the fissure cavity which lies between them. In the species with pale eggs this is the stage at which dark pigment first appears. The amount of pigment in the pigment epithelium increases slightly, until there is a sharp rise with the onset of the circulation. Afterwards there is a further increase. It starts in the dorsal part of the eye; the iris and the ventral part of the eye darken later, and the margin of the pupil and the area of the eye fissure even later still.

Pigmentation occurs in the experimental material as it does normally. Pigment appears as the external layer of the eye becomes thinner and as the mesenchyme comes to surround it. It increases noticeably as the circulation starts, and this increase is particularly striking in urodeles in which, unlike anurans, pigmentation does not increase in the absence of blood.

It was first noticed by Spemann (1912) that the increase of pigment in the pigment epithelium took place at the same time as the formation and extrusion of pigment from the retina. This is difficult to see in the eyes of normal embryos, where the pigment epithelium and retina are closely pressed together; but where cavities are formed within retinal tissue or between the retina and the epithelium, the scale of the phenomenon can be clearly seen. It can be observed in living and fixed explants (Chapter II, section 2, Figs. 5, 6, 7, 8), in eyes explanted in mesenchyme-ectoderm coats (Chapter III, section 2, Figs. 15, 16, 19, 23, 24, 26), and in grafts of eye rudiments into whole embryos (Chapter III, section 3, Figs. 32, 34, 35, 40, 41, 46, 58), especially in species with pale eggs. The granules continue to emerge until the visual outgrowths have formed.

They always emerge from the surface of the retina where most mitoses are found (Fig. 45) and where the visual outgrowths will later form. All these phenomena also occur around each intraretinal cavity no matter how the cavity has arisen, which suggests that essential conditions for their appearance are created when retinal surfaces come to face the internal eye cavities. The reversal of the polarity of the early retina by its experimental inversion within the eye, which causes its surface earlier directed towards the lens to be directed towards the pigment epithelium (Eakin, 1947), is in accordance with these data.

The development of the pigment epithelium and retina are not only antagonistic, but at first include processes which are common to the whole eye rudiment. Later the density of pigment intensifes in the pigment epithelium and declines, by extrusion, in the retina, and this distinction increases right up to the formation of the visual outgrowths — in fact for as long as the retina still has the capacity to form pigment epithelium, to change its polarity, and to induce a lens (Chapter III, section 4). Retinal cells evidently become intolerant of pigment granules and their precursors, and reject the granules when acquiring their typical internal structure.

To summarize, it may be said that while the facts learnt from normal development agree with those discovered experimentally, they cannot be fully understood without experiments. The unfolding of the mechanisms of eye development falls into two periods, the first of which ends at about the onset of circulation in the eye and the separation of layers in the retina. This period also sees the formation of the mesenchyme coats and the shaping of the eye as a whole, together with its pigmentation. The relationship between these two periods varies with the species, as has already been described.

The complex of phenomena which were discovered by the experiments described in this chapter leave however some problems outstanding and these must be solved for a full understanding of eye development. Is the separation of the rudiment into pigment epithelium and retina caused only because the distal pole is protected from, and the proximal one exposed to, the influence of the mesenchyme — or what other conditions are responsible? What produces the cup shape of the retina? The next chapter analyses these questions.

CHAPTER IV

The Significance of the Connexion of the Eye Rudiment with Ectoderm and Lens, in the Development of the Eye

1. Introduction

This chapter examines the importance of the connexions between the eye rudiment and the ectoderm, and between the eye rudiment and the lens which arises from the ectoderm during development. It is not surprising that these connexions play a very important part in the development of the eye: the eye rudiment is in contact with the ectoderm from the start of its development, and the lens which develops at the point of contact becomes incorporated into the structure of the eye. Furthermore, it is of course that part of the eye rudiment which lies in contact with the ectoderm which later forms retina.

Spemann (1901, 1906) and Lewis (1904, 1907) discovered that the formation of a lens depended on the influence of the eye. Dragomirov (1936, 1937, 1939), Mikami (1939a) and other workers discovered reciprocal dependencies, by showing that the contact of the ectoderm with the eye rudiment led to the subsequent development of retina at these points of contact. In Chapter II, it was shown that crowded conditions can cause the cells in the rudiment to turn into retina without any contact with the ectoderm, but this does not mean that there are no influences that stimulate and localize such crowding. The ectoderm may for instance encourage parts of the rudiment to develop into retina by protecting them from contact with mesenchyme over the area which it covers (Chapter III). Is this the extent of the function of the ectoderm, or does the actual contact help the crowding of the cells? How does the cup shape of the retina originate, if it can after all develop other shapes? And why is there such a strong tendency for the rudiment to form retina at the place where it is in contact with the ectoderm?

The experiments which were carried out to answer these questions are described in the following sections; a comparison is made between

88

results of retaining and of breaking the link between the eye rudiment
and the lens forming material, and the changes in the relations between
eye rudiment, lens and ectoderm which occur during development
are discussed.

2. How the Eye Rudiment Developing in Saline is Affected by the Presence of Lens-Ectoderm

In these experiments, eyes were explanted in saline, either with
or without lens-ectoderm, according to the techniques, and with the
general results described in Chapter II, section 2. Particular attention
was paid to the influence exerted by the lens, especially on the
formation of the retina.

In urodeles, at the time of the operation, the optic vesicle is loosely
stuck to, and just separable from, the single-layered ectoderm. If it
was necessary to retain the lens-forming material in the eye, a piece
of ectoderm was left on the distal part of the eye rudiments. Anurans
have a two layered ectoderm which Dettlaff (1938–1947) has studied
in detail. It consists of a thin but compact outer layer, and a friable
inner layer. A group of cells from the inner layer, which later gives
rise to the lens, sticks closely to the outer, lateral surface of the eye
rudiment. In these, therefore, the difficulty comes rather in removing
the lens-forming material from the rudiment than in leaving it.

In *B. viridis*, *R. esculenta*, *R. arvalis* and *Pelobates* at the optic
vesicle stage, lens-forming cells were removed with difficulty, for it was
impossible to detach it without cutting part of the surface of the eye.
In *R. arvalis*, and particularly in *Bufo viridis* the operation was often
easily carried out. These observations are also relevant to the experiments in subsequent sections of this chapter. After two days in saline,
some of the eyes, including all the axolotl eyes with lens-ectoderm,
were grafted into embryos. These results are described in Chapter IV,
section 4.

The formation of eye rudiments even in the absence of the lens
differs from species to species. In newts, the surface of the retinal
parts of explants remains even and rounded throughout its development (Fig. 2, g–j), and lacks any sort of invagination. Sections of the
elongated body show that the fissure cavity which lies along the long
axis is often straight, sometimes)(-shaped or (-shaped: a diagram
is given in Fig. 9a. The walls are of uniform thickness, and there
is no marked polarity in the cells (Fig. 5). In axolotls, the majority

of the eyes develop in a similar way, and the rounded surface is kept throughout development. In a few, however, a slight invagination (Fig. 2,e) appears on the surface of the explants, but it disappears in later development. In sections these axolotl eyes resemble the newt eyes; but occasionally one of the walls in the (-shaped fissure type is considerably thicker than the other (Fig. 9, b). This is the only sign of invagination ever observed on the surface of the explants. No lens ever arose if the explant did not contain lens-octoderm.

In *Bufo viridis* not a single lens developed after the lens-forming cells had been carefully removed. Two zones can be distinguished in the yellowish retina of the developing explants: in some of them a narrow invagination can be seen in the centre of the paler zone (Fig. 3). The structure of these anuran eyes appears more variable than the urodele eye in sections and this is true of the smaller number of eyes with walls of uniform thickness (Fig. 9,b), and of the eyes whose thicker wall is separated from its thinner wall by a half-moon shaped fissure (Fig. 6). In the eyes of *R. arvalis* and of *B. viridis* from which lenses have been removed (the development is shown in Fig. 4) the retina often separates after 2–3 days cultivation into two zones. In the centre of the paler zone is either a shallow, well defined depression (Fig. 4, C, IV) or a light spot lying on the edge of the brain: this is apparently a part of the pale retinal zone, much narrowed as a result of invagination inside the eye. In the course of later development these depressions become invisible. Numerous mitoses which can be seen in sections of 24-hour explants also disappear later on. Of thirty-one lens-free explants, which were fixed within a few days of explantation, the majority showed a thin wall lying opposite a thick wall, particularly in those cases in which a narrow cavity, usually crescent shaped, lay opposite the bottom of the depression (Fig. 7). If there is no invagination the variation in the thickness of the walls is less marked. Sometimes parts of the walls fused together and the fissures became divided into compartments; other variations were noticed, which indicate the instability of the processes which produce the structure of the explanted eye. Finally, in some eyes the original differences in the thickness of the wall are lost, and a three-chambered fissure arises, i.e. three thickenings begin to develop which are united by thin pieces. This type of eye resembles some of the rudiments which developed in mesenchyme surroundings (Chapter III, section 2). A diagrammatic scheme of these types of structure is given in Fig. 9,d.

Unlike this series, the experiments on twenty *Rana arvalis* eyes with lenses showed great uniformity of eye structure. The lens is shaped like a globe, and is made up of radially arranged cells, which are not differentiated into lens nucleus and lens epithelium. It lies centrally, and is enveloped by a layer of retina whose edges meet, so that the lens is completely surrounded (Fig. 8, a).

In seventeen of the experiments, the eye consisted of a single layer of well polarized retina, without the fissure cavity which usually separates the two eye layers. The remnant of a cavity was found in the retinal wall in only three cases and was, as usual, filled with pigment (Fig. 9, e); in these eyes, the lens was merged with the retina. Where the retina consisted of a single uninterrupted layer, pigment emerged from its outer surface (Fig. 8, b).

In one example (Fig. 8, c), where the wall of the eye rudiment was stuck to the glass by its lens, the lens lay in a cup-like retina, whose edges were prevented from uniting by the glass. The brain pendant lay to one side; normally it closes the aperture between the edges of the inturning retina. Though the glass prevented the edge of the retina from curling up, the eye developed an approximately normal shape.

The Basal Sheet and the Rolling up of the Retina

When a lens is present the retina rolls and invaginates normally, but even when it is absent the processes occur to some extent. This may be because the forces which cause the retina to roll up are applied to the substrate which still remains when the lens has been removed. When the connexions with the lens—or, earlier, with the ectoderm— are absent, this rolling occurs in species in which the retinal zone has already acquired some stability; we may therefore suppose that this substrate helps to establish the position of the retina in the eye rudiment. In lens-free, invaginated eyes, and in a series of similar cases described in the next section, a thin layer of material can be seen lying on the internal surface of the retina, and uniting the ends of its cells; it usually appears after 2 to 3 days in culture, but perhaps arises even earlier. It turns dark grey on staining with blue black B, and evidently corresponds to the pale yellow central zone of those explanted retinas in some part of which invagination takes place. It is possible that the attachment of this layer to the ends of the cells acts as a focal point upon which the stretching forces can act; it is also probable that the layer may itself evoke polarity in the

developing retinal cells: in support of this is the fact that polarity
is most evident when the thin layer is present and that isolated cells
of the neural plate lengthen and become polarized if a small piece
of the protein surface coat of the plate remains attached at one end
(Holtfreter, 1946, 1947, 1948 b). It corresponds to the basal membrane
of the early mammalian retina described by Dejean (1939) and by
Rochon-Duvigneaud (1943); this membrane stains a similar colour
with napthol black, and has a cuticular structure which envelops the
ends of most of the cells. The function of this layer in the formation
and development of the retina was discovered by experiment; it
should be called the bottom or basal sheet in order to distinguish it
from the basement membrane of the epidermis. Further experiments
and observations give a fuller description of the part played by the
basal sheet in the development of the eye.

A study of the differences in behaviour between lens-free and lens-
bearing eyes of different species makes it possible to draw some
conclusions about the importance of the lens and of the ectoderm in
eye formation. After the eye rudiment separates from the ectoderm
one of its walls thickens and displays some tendency to invaginate;
but these phenomena are clearly shown only in anurans. The cupping
is much enhanced when lens-forming ectoderm is available; a lens
then develops, and this is followed by the assumption of an exaggerated cup shape by the retina, and by its closing up around the
lens. This last process is probably connected with the separation of
the eye from the ectoderm: this normally prevents complete rolling
up of the retina, and so restricts the shape of the cup.

The importance of the lens-ectoderm and of the lens which arises
from it in the process of shaping the retina is that they increase the
development of the basal sheet, which helps the retina to roll up,
and that they themselves act as supports in the rolling process.

3. How the Development of Eye Rudiments in Ectoderm-Mes-
enchyme Explants Depends on the Presence of a Connexion with
Lens-Ectoderm

In a previous section, we described how the development of eyes
explanted into saline varied with the species and with the availability
of lens-ectoderm. In this section an attempt is made to study what
happens when the connexions with the ectoderm remain unbroken, and
what happens when the connexion is absent and the eye rudiment is

explanted surrounded by mesenchyme and ectoderm. These experiments should also explain how the influence of the mesenchyme on the eye rudiment varies according to the amount of rolling up of the retina.

In these experiments, eye rudiments were wrapped in pure neurula ectoderm, both with and without lens-ectoderm. They sometimes developed without mesenchyme, but more often with a surrounding of mesenchyme which arose from the rudiment itself. These experiments, and a series in which sources of mesoderm or ecto-mesenchyme were added to the explant, form a basic group in which the explants contained only small amounts of mesenchyme; for this series newts, axolotls, *Rana arvalis* and *Rana ridibunda* were used, and the results showed how the development of the cup shape is affected by the availability of lens-forming material.

A second series of experiments used only axolotls. In these experiments the ectoderm was removed from the embryonic head at the optic vesicle stage. In some the vesicles remained attached to the ectoderm, while in others they were freed from it and then rewrapped. The neural crest was kept, and large quantities of ectomesenchyme emerged from it, so that its amount in the explants was almost normal. In this way the importance of keeping an unbroken connexion between the eye rudiment and the ectoderm of the whole head could be estimated, and not merely its connexion with the small lens-forming part. The methods used were those described in Chapter III, section 2, but here some series were also included in which the connexion between the eye rudiment and the lens-forming ectoderm was retained.

In the explants deprived of mesenchyme, eye rudiments developed in the same way as if explanted into saline. The eight newt eye rudiments already described in Chapter III differed from these explants only in that their cavity was somewhat enlarged; in two cases lenses developed from the ectoderm but they did not cause the rudiment to become cup-shaped (Fig. 15). Cupping in fact develops when lens-forming material is left within the eye rudiment. In every case, the half-moon shaped fissure cavity (Fig. 59) lay on the side opposite to the lens. The lens merges with the ectoderm and keeps its connexions with the eye; this can be seen particularly well in the ten cases in which the eye has emerged from its ectodermal coat, but remains attached to the ectoderm by the lens. The structure of the eye in these examples was similar to those just described.

The closed axolotl explants of lens-free eye rudiments without mesenchyme resemble the naked explants, and consist of a mass of cells with a centrally placed fissure cavity. The picture changes sharply if a piece of lens-forming ectoderm is incorporated. All the eyes which contained a little mesenchyme remained attached by the lens to the ectodermal coat when they emerged from it. These eyes consisted of strongly polarized retina, without an internal cavity; they curled around the lens, and resembled the frog's eyes, complete with lens material, which developed in saline. The polarization of the retina under the influence of lens-ectoderm is here much more marked than it is in newts.

How the Formation of the Eye Depends on its Attachments to Lens-Ectoderm, in the Presence of Mesenchyme and Ectoderm

By estimating the extent to which they have achieved a definitive cup shape, the eyes in these explants can be related to one of five types of eye structure, as shown in Table 10. These types take into account not only the shape of the cup, but also the swelling of the eye, and the development of its walls into pigment epithelium or retina. The examples which developed adherent to the bottom of the glass, and were thus restricted for space, are shown separately.

In newts, only eye rudiments without presumptive lens material were used, and when lenses developed, they came from other ectoderm. Lenses appeared in twenty-three out of thirty examples, and sometimes two lenses, and once three, were found in a single explant. In the free-swimming explants, however, the retina became cup-shaped just as often whether there was a lens (29 per cent) or not (21 per cent). The remaining retinas did not become cup-shaped, and in most cases the secondary lenses seem to have no effect on the shape of the eye (Figs. 16, 17, 22). If these newt eyes do become at all cupped, they do so on a small scale, as is shown by the fact that the outer layer of the eye, which lies against the cup-like retina, does not develop into pigment epithelium; in two cases, eyes of this type developed even when the lens was absent (Fig. 19), and in four cases, when it was present. The attachment of newt explants to the glass did not favour their adopting a cup shape (three cases).

In axolotls, lenses do not develop in trunk ectoderm exposed to the influence of the eye; and because of this they provide useful material for studying the part played by the contacts between the presumptive lens material and the eye rudiment in eye formation.

In the first group of experiments, axolotl eye rudiments were wrapped in abdominal ectoderm and explanted, either with or without small pieces of lens-forming material, and with a small quantity of mesenchyme. A cup shape was achieved by only 19 per cent of the free swimming explants which lacked presumptive lens material, but by 60 per cent of those which included it.

This quantitative difference does not define sufficiently clearly the conditions necessary for the formation of the eye. In six out of eight of the lens-free, cup-shaped eyes the retina was turned to the ectoderm, and was not separated from it by mesenchyme cells; in a few cases, however, there was a thin layer of mesenchyme of the inner cornea — this normally develops after the lens has separated from the ectoderm. The cup shape is less pronounced in the free swimming explants (Fig. 23, b), and though it is more noticeable in those developing on glass (Fig. 24) it still does not match the definitive cup shape achieved by eyes with lenses explanted into saline. There is therefore good reason to suppose that the cup shape depends on the contact between the eye rudiment and the ectoderm, as does the positioning of the retina (Dragomirov, 1939), and that it increases with the strength of the contact. There is also some system of mechanical ties between the retina and the ectoderm which prevents mesenchyme from filling the space left between them when they separate.

Though the majority of eyes with lenses are cup-like, the shape is no more pronounced than it is in the swimming explants which lack lenses (Fig. 20). The whole of the proximal eye wall does not always develop into pigment epithelium; it does when the cup shape is more accentuated, as for example in the lens-free explants attached to glass. The lenses are attached not only to the concave surface of the retina, but also to the ectoderm of the explant. The importance of these connexions in shaping the eye is illustrated by the two cases exemplified by Type 2, Table 10; here the lens is also attached to the ectoderm, but the eye, which lies at some little distance from it, is stretched lengthways in the direction of the lens, and only a small depression at the apex of its extended end shows a tendency to become cupped. In a third case (Type 5, Table 10) a part of the retina which lies beside the lens is slightly pulled out towards the ectoderm, as if it were at an early stage in the process of developing into one of the stretched eyes. These observations confirm the existence of mechanical attachments between lens and retina. The developing mechanical

Types of eye-structure	Diagrammatic examples
1. Thick-walled vesicle of retina, no pigt. epithm., walls not cup-shaped	
2. Retinal fragments connected with pieces of pigt. epithm., no cup-shape	
3. Vesicle of pigt. epithm., parts of whose wall contain fragments of retina or brain	
4. Retinal vesicle with one wall thicker than the other, slightly cup-shaped	
5. More or less cup-shaped retina (1—2) covered with pigt. epithm.	
Total	

* These explants developed attached to the bottom of the culture vessel, which caused stretching in the ectoderm.

Explanted in Epidermal-Mesenchyme Vesicles differs between Connexions with Lens-Forming Ectoderm

Experiments with restricted quantity of mesenchyme and trunk ectoderm								Experiments with large quantities of mesenchyme and head ectoderm	
Newts		Axolotls		*Rana arvalis*		*Rana ridibunda*		Axolotls	
without lenses	with secondary lens	without lenses	with primary lens	without lenses	with lens	without lenses	with primary lens	separated from ectoderm	links with ectoderm kept
3	7 + 1*	10	—	1	—	—	—	—	—
2	6	9	3	1	2	—	—	2	—
—	2	6	1	4	2	—	1	10	2
2	4 + 3*	—	1	—	—	—	—	—	—
—	—	6 + 3*	5	5	6	1	5	2	10
7	19 + 4*	31 + 3*	10	11	10**	1	6	14	12

** In 2 cases from groups 3 and 5 the lens-forming cells were removed, and the lens developed from the ectoderm.

ties between ectoderm, lens, and eye, can, according to circumstances, lead either to the formation of a cup-shaped retina (in conjunction with the influence of the ectoderm on the eye rudiment), or to a breakdown of the cup shape; they also restrict the extent to which the retina can roll up by preventing it from surrounding the lens.

In the second group of experiments on axolotls, the eye vesicle was either left on the ectoderm which had been removed from the head of the embryo at the eye vesicle stage, or it was separated from it and then rewrapped. The eyes in the first of these two series appear cupped, even to external inspection (Fig. 25). Actually, 85 per cent of the eyes in this series become cupped, while in the series in which the eyes were separated from the ectoderm the figure dropped to 14 per cent.

Lenses developed in 50 per cent of the experiments in which axolotl head ectoderm was wrapped around explants of eye rudiments, probably because this ectoderm had already come under the influence of the eye before operation. These lenses do not normally affect the shape of the eye, but in those cases which develop without a pronounced cup shape, there is also no mesenchyme between the ectoderm, lens and retina. The lens is attached to the ectoderm and to the edges of the retinal invagination by extremely fine extra-cellular threads.

The great variation in the eye structure in this series of explants contrasts with the uniform results obtained when the eye rudiments were not separated from the ectoderm (Fig. 27). These eyes are cup shaped, but not to any marked extent; the lens lies in the centre of the cup and is joined to its edges by well-defined extra-cellular threads; in some cases, the lenses are also connected to the ectoderm by similar threads, and in others, a mesenchyme layer, or inner cornea, already lies between the lens and the ectoderm. Mesenchyme is always absent from the space between the retina and the ectoderm in which the lens and the threads are arranged. Only two of the ex-planted eyes were not cup shaped, and in one of them, the lens appeared attached to the bottom of the retina, and had pulled the retina behind it. In another explant only one very enlarged eye was found; probably the internal pressure, exerted in conditions of unrestricted space, destroyed the cup shape of the retina.

In *Rana arvalis* the experiment is complicated by the fact that a part of the eye evokes the formation of new lenses from the ecto-derm. A comparison of the percentage which become cup-shaped in eye rudiments with and without lenses shows that there is little difference between the two groups: in the group without lenses, 45 per cent become cup-shaped, and in the group with lenses, 60 per cent—that is, as many as in the comparable experiments on axolotls. All the *Rana ridibunda* eye rudiments were explanted with lens-forming material and almost all (83 per cent) of the eyes became cup-shaped.* In anurans, as experiments on *Rana arvalis* showed,

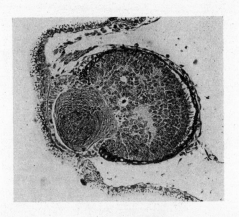

FIG. 58. Apical part of eye rudiment of *Pelobates* grafted under the ectoderm of an embryo. Shown 6 days after operation. The retina has differentiated into layers, irregularly arranged, because they are broken up by small cavities, lined with visual cells and outgrowths. The pigment epithelium is surrounded by a mesenchyme coat, in which erythrocytes can be seen.

the cup shape is achieved in a large percentage of cases, and its frequency does not vary much with the presence or absence of the lens. Since one wall of the lens-free anuran eye rudiment explanted in saline appears considerably thicker than the other, lens-forming material obviously only increases the tendency of the wall to thicken and roll into a cup.

The majority of cup-like eyes, whether they have a lens or not (Fig. 30, 60; Fig. 31), are shallow, and the wall of pigment epithelium is sometimes unclosed. A few of them have a flat or convex retina, and could almost belong to Group 3. The lenses are as a rule attached to both retina and ectoderm. In two cases where the lenses were

---

* One case does not fit into this category, because its retina was flat; in one eye, without a lens, an additional retina developed at the point where it was in contact with the ectoderm (Fig. 60).

pulled out away from the ectoderm, it was possible to see that the attachment was effected by extra-cellular threads. The lenses almost always lie laterally beside the slightly cup-shaped retinas (Fig. 31), and are sometimes stretched out in the form of strands to the place where they unite with the ectoderm. In three cases an additional

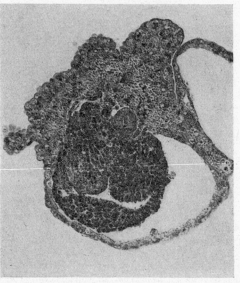

FIG. 59. Newt eye rudiment, explanted with pieces of lens-ectoderm, which has developed into retina in the absence of mesenchyme. The cavity of the eye isolates the thick part of the retina which adjoins the lens. Shown 7 days after explantation.

depression is formed beside the point of contact between lens and retina. Apparently the lenses which only have a small area of contact with the retina exert a correspondingly small effect on the formation of the cup shape. In a single instance, where the cup is deeper, the lens enters symmetrically into the curvature of the cup and fills it, while still attached to the ectoderm.

The Part Played in Eye Formation by the Stability of the Retinal Zone of the Eye Rudiment, and by the Basal Sheet

In the closed vesicle-like explants, either with or without a lens, the progress of the retina towards its final cup shape never exceeds the level normally achieved at the onset of the circulation when the

cavity between the lens and the retina is formed. This is to be expected, since there is no blood in these explants. They differ
noticeably from eye rudiments explanted in saline, in which the cup

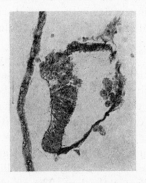

FIG. 60. Eye rudiment of *Rana ridibunda* explanted enveloped in late
gastrula ectoderm. One of the two retinas which formed is shown in
the photograph; they are united by a common pigment epithelium.
A clearly defined basal sheet lies on the surface of the retina. Mesenchyme cells lie on the surface of the pigment epithelium. Shown 5 days
after explantation.

shape develops exaggeratedly when a lens is present; but here too it is
the connexions with lens-ectoderm which increase the frequency of
the appearance of the cup shape, particularly in axolotls.

The basal sheet (Fig. 60) could be seen in cup-shaped retinas which
faced the ectoderm if the explant was fixed before the stage at which
the retina segregated into layers and the visual outgrowths developed,
and it was especially visible if the lens was absent. In later stages
it is absent from the centre of the retina, but may still be found in
the marginal, iris region, where the layers have not yet segregated;
from this point fine threads connect the iris to the lens (Fig. 27). This
supports the earlier conclusion that the basal sheet helps the retina
to roll into a cup shape (Chapter IV, section 2) and indicates that it
arises where the eye rudiment comes into contact with the ectoderm.

After the eye rudiment has separated from the ectoderm, the
degree of stability in the retina and pigment epithelium zones in
saline varies from species to species; this is probably because the
basal sheet develops earlier in the retinal zone of some species.
Accordingly in anurans, where stability in the retina arises early, the

presence of a lens only slightly accentuates the cup shaping of the retinal zone; in axolotls, where stability occurs later, the role of the contact with the ectoderm in assisting cupping can be seen particularly clearly. In newts the basal sheet forms late, and plays a relatively small part in the development of the cup form, and so the contact with the ectoderm in the explants influences the shape of the eye only slightly.

It has already been shown that the part played in the formation of the eye by the connexions between the lens-ectoderm and the eye rudiment changes during development. Until the lens is formed, the ectoderm promotes the development of the basal sheet, and consequently the stability of the retinal zone and its ability to curl up. In different species they grow at different rates, and the eye of each requires a different length of contact. By its attachment to the retina, the developing lens assists and controls the rolling up process in the retina, so that it embraces the lens. The effects of the basal sheet and of the lens are thus in this sense equivalent, but the relative importance of each varies from species to species.

The Role of the Connexions between Ectoderm, Lens and Retina in the Formation of the Eye

A description has already been given of how the connexions between the ectoderm and the eye persist but change as the lens develops. Almost all the lenses introduced with the eye rudiment are pulled out towards the ectoderm, and are united with it. The actual lenses which arise from the ectoderm are attached to the retina. The mechanical strength of the attachments can be seen when the ectoderm is pulled away from the eye: the eye then stretches, its shape changes and the cup form is lost; both this and the results from earlier experiments on isolated heads show why it is that in *Rana arvalis*, in which the connexions between the lens and the ectoderm do not break down, the eye is noticeably elongated, and in *Rana esculenta* and axolotls, in which the lenses are separate from the ectoderm (Chapter III, section 5), this is not the case. The way in which the extra-cellular threads achieve these results can be seen when the lens is removed from the ectoderm and from the retina (Fig. 27).

The mechanical ties which unite the retina of the eye rudiment to the lens, and the lens to the ectoderm, obviously play an important part in the development of the eye, according to the environmental conditions. They enhance the rolling up of the retina by their attachment to the lens, and at the same time prevent it from rolling too far, due to the contact of the edges of the retina with the ectoderm conditioned by this mechanical connection. If the ectoderm is displaced the cup shape of the eye may be completely lost.

The mesenchyme contained in explants also influences the extent of rolling up of the retina by affecting the degree of swelling of the explants. In free-swimming explants the stretching of the eye rudiments by their internal secretion, when they are surrounded by mesenchyme, reduces the extent of the cup-shaping. The development of the pigment epithelium, which is also dependent on the influence of the mesenchyme, also varies according to whether or not the retina is noticeably cup-shaped. In the first group of axolotl explants the eye rudiments which had developed in a restricted space became most cup-shaped, and their whole outer wall developed into pigment epithelium; in the free swimming explants in which the eyes were only slightly cup-shaped, not all the outer wall developed into pigment epithelium. If the cup shape was completely lost, or if the eye was elongated, pigment epithelium was either lacking or formed only at the apex of the cavity, where it increased in area only in very swollen eyes. This means that in the absence of conditions causing unusual enlargement, the amount of pigment epithelium which develops depends on whether the cup shape of the retina is marked or not. As the retina rolls up, it stretches the outer layer of the eye, thus helping it to develop into pigment epithelium by promoting the influence of the mesenchyme. When space is restricted, and the layers lie closely against each other, this effect is particularly well marked. These regularities do not hold good for newt development, because here the cup shape does not develop without prolonged and unbroken contact with the ectoderm.

Cupping develops most fully when the space is limited and the cells are consequently crowded; then most of the rudiment, except its outer wall, develops into retina. While curling up of the retina promotes the development of pigment epithelium by stretching its cells, the formation of the pigment epithelium in its turn promotes the rolling up of the retina, unless the eye enlarges. Thus, under experimental conditions which approach to normal, we can see how the different developmental processes work together, and increase each other's influence in the process of building up normal eye structures.

8*

It is now possible to point out the most important of the regularities which emerge from the various facts described in this section.
When the eye is surrounded by mesenchyme and ectoderm, the cup
shape is never exaggerated. The frequency of cup-shaped eyes
increases after uninterrupted contact with lens-ectoderm, because
a continuous contact leads to progressive development of the basal
sheet, which assists the retina to roll up. When the lens has left the
ectoderm it is still attached to the retina and the ectoderm, and this
both helps the retina to roll up and at the same time restricts this
movement to the amount necessary to form the normal primary
optic cup. As the cup shape develops and space is at the same
time restricted, the differentiation of pigment epithelium, under the
influence of the mesenchyme, extends over the whole proximal wall
of the eye; it does not however go beyond it, as can be seen when the
rudiment has swollen inside its mesenchyme surrounding. When the
connexions between the eye rudiment and the lens-ectoderm are
unbroken, in a restricted environment, the different processes involved are able to establish the eye in its most typical form.

4. How the Development of the Eye Rudiment in Embryos depends on the Presence or Absence of the Lens

In order to establish whether the regularities observed in the connexions between ectoderm, lens and eye in experimental material
also apply to normal embryonic development, grafts of eye rudiments,
either with or without presumptive lens, were placed in whole embryos,
and in the "hemi-embryos" which were described in Chapter III,
section 3. Grafts of eye rudiments were placed into different parts
of the body, including the brain cavity, and grafts were also
made of eye rudiments which had been first explanted into saline
for 2, and occasionally, 3 days. Two hundred eyes from newts,
axolotls, *Rana arvalis*, *Rana ridibunda*, *Bufo viridis*, and *Pelobates*
were examined. The material was fixed at different stages, and the
tables and surveys include urodele eye rudiments which had lived
for more than 6 days, and anurans which had lived for more than
4 days. A small number were fixed at 4 to 6 days or earlier. The
operative techniques were those described in Chapter III, sections 3–4.
When eye rudiments are grafted into embryos, the environment depends
on whether they are in the body cavity, where there is no mesenchyme, or in the subcutaneous mesenchyme of the body, or in the head,

where they are surrounded by mesenchyme. When grafted into hemi-embryos where there is less mesenchyme, the eyes are in an environment which is very like that in the body cavity.

Development of Eye Rudiments Grafted Directly into Embryos and Hemi-Embryos

Table 11 gives figures showing how the cup shape of the eye rudiments depends on the attachment between them and the lenses. In newts, however, lenses usually developed when lens-free eye rudiments were grafted. Apart from this, the shape also depends upon other conditions, and particularly on the eye's position in the embryo. These must therefore also be taken into account.

In newts lenses developed, not only in four cases from which lens-ectoderm had been removed, but in every case except one—viz. in twenty-two out of twenty-three. There was no difference between the formation of eyes containing lens-ectoderm and the other eyes. When the eye rudiment contained a lens, either cup-shaped eyes, or eyes without any cup shape at all might develop. The clearest cup shape was achieved in five eyes, in which the lens fitted closely into the curvature of the optic cup (Fig. 43). Lenses do not always

TABLE 11

Estimates of the Cup Shape in Eyes Developing with or without Lenses, Grafted into Embryos or Hemi-Embryos

Species		Cup shape absent	Cup shape slightly marked	Cup shape well marked	Cup shape exaggerated
Triturus	without lenses	—	1	—	—
	with lenses	9	8	5	—
Axolotl	without lenses	31	10	2	—
	with lenses	—	4	4	—
Rana	without lenses	—	1	—	—
arvalis	with lenses	—	5	12	3
Bufo	without lenses	7	2	—	—
viridis	with lenses	—	—	—	—
Rana	without lenses	—	2	—	—
ridibunda	with lenses	—	1	3	—
Pelobates	without lenses	—	—	—	—
	with lenses	—	1	4	—

develop from the ectoderm which lies directly opposite the eye; in some cases the invagination of the cup faced inwards, and the origin of the lens from the ectoderm was marked by a chain of ecto-dermal nodules, representing the remains of the former attach-ments between the lens and the ectoderm. Cup-shaped and non-cup-shaped eyes are found in the subcutaneous mesenchyme, and in the body cavity. The primary cavity is not lost in the explants inside the body cavity, and as in the newt eye rudiments with lenses explanted without mesenchyme (Chapter III, section 2), it becomes crescent-shaped (Fig. 43).

The forty-three axolotl eyes without lenses differ noticeably from the eight which were grafted with pieces of lens-ectoderm. In axolotls, lenses do not develop from the host ectoderm, so these eyes remain without lenses. While 72 per cent of eyes without lenses fail to be-come cup-shaped, all the eyes grafted with lenses become cupped. The majority of lens-free, non-cup-shaped eyes lie in the body cavity (Fig. 34) and only a few are found outside (Fig. 37). Four eyes of this type, however, lie in the surrounding mesenchyme and are covered by pigment epithelium. Twelve cup-shaped eyes without lenses are surrounded by mesenchyme and their invagination is usually turned towards the ectoderm (Fig. 61); in four cases it is turned either to-wards the intestines, or to the inside of the head (Fig. 39). Eight grafts of axolotl eye rudiments with lens-forming material were transplanted into the mesenchyme or body cavity of hemi-embryos, where they all became cup-shaped. The least cup-shaped eye was stretched between the ectoderm and endoderm (Fig. 41) and resembled the explanted eyes already described in Chapter IV, section 3. The cup shape was nowhere exaggerated (Fig. 40). The lenses in these eyes were not connected to the ectoderm, but in half of them the lenses are attached by ectodermal pendants, evidently consisting of ecto-derm which does not enter into the structure of the lens. In some cases, small additional retinas developed in the middle of the pigment epithelium which developed when the outer layer of the eye was surrounded by mesenchyme. A case in which a retina developed at the point of contact with the pronephros is shown in Fig. 40.

In *Rana arvalis* lens-forming cells were not removed from the eye rudiments, and out of twenty-one cases only one had no lens. All the eyes were cup-shaped whether they lay in an environment of mesenchyme, or partly in the body cavity and partly in the mesenchyme. The six eyes grafted into hemi-embryos were less cup-shaped than those grafted into whole embryos; of these latter the three which were partly in the body cavity became perfectly cup-shaped (Fig. 44). In these examples the lens was not attached to any substrate. In other examples, the lens was attached either to the ectoderm or to the intestines, and the eye was typically cupped, except in one case. In this the lens was attached to the intestines, and was stretched out behind them away from the region of the pupil. The eyes in the

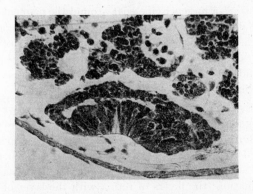

FIG. 61. Axolotl eye rudiment grafted under the epidermis of the abdominal region of an embryo. There are two walls of retinal material, separated by the fissure cavity; the wall facing the ectoderm is the thicker and is slightly cupped, its cells are polarized, and their ends are united by the basal sheet. Shown 6 days after operation.

hemi-embryos are characterized by the absence of a cavity between the lens and the retina, while in whole embryos a well developed cavity forms between them. This distinction is obviously caused by the difference in the blood supply (Chapter III, section 3).

Lens-forming cells were also not removed from the eyes of six *Rana ridibunda*, but lenses failed to develop in two of them. All the eyes were grafted into whole embryos, and developed surrounded by mesenchyme in the subcutaneous layer. The cup shape was nowhere exaggerated and was only slightly developed in the two lens-free eyes, and in one which had a lens. In all these eyes, with the exception of one which lacked a lens and was scarcely cup-shaped, the retina was turned towards the ectoderm.

The *Pelobates* eyes were also grafted with lens-material. Most of them were grafted between the outer and inner layers of the ectoderm which in this species, unlike other amphibia, are hardly connected at all. However, the majority of the eyes were extruded from the surface of the embryo in an ectodermal bag, and finally, only five remained to be examined.

The lenses in all these grafted eyes were relatively larger than in the other species investigated (Fig. 42). All developed surrounded by mesenchyme; there was very little mesenchyme in the eyes lying in the independent ectodermal extrusions, and in these cases it was very difficult to trace a mesenchyme coat around the pigment epithelium. It could be detected only because it turned into inner cornea at the lens, as in a series of experiments described earlier. In two eyes the lens was pressed against the intestines and fused with them, and the connexion did not subsequently break down. In one case this led to a reduction in the cup shape.

To contrast with the previous anuran species, eye rudiments without lens-forming material from ten *Bufo viridis* were grafted into the body cavity of hemi-embryos. The majority developed as spherical masses of cells with an inner cavity, towards which the layer of visual cells was turned (Fig. 35). In two cases there was a narrow, deep invagination; the layers of retina with the layer of visual cells along the outer surface were arranged concentrically in relation to this invagination (Fig. 36). This picture exactly matches that of lens-free anuran eyes developing in fluid environments, except that in these eyes, a layer of visual cells developed on the surface of the eye. A comparison of these results with the experiments in which the eye rudiment was grafted with its lens shows that in whole embryos the presence of the lens increases the frequency and extent of cupping, though sometimes this may be partially achieved even without a lens.

The Development of the Eye Rudiment in the Cavity of the Embryonic Brain

Five eye rudiments of *Rana esculenta* were grafted with lens-forming material into the forebrain cavity of embryos of the same age; all the grafts became attached to the brain roof. The cup shape became exaggerated. There was no pigment epithelium on the surface of the eye which faced into the brain cavity. These results fully confirm those of Dragomirov (1935a), and show that in the fluid medium of the brain cavity the frog eye rudiment develops as it does in the body cavity.

The Development of Lens-Bearing and Lens-Free Eye Rudiments in Whole Embryos after Preliminary Explantation

The general results of the development of eye rudiments after preliminary explantation are described in Chapter III, section 4. The present section is concerned to show how the differences in development depend on whether or not the presumptive lens has been removed. A series of experiments was set up on axolotls, *Rana arvalis* and *Rana ridibunda*.

All the axolotl eye rudiments were grafted into embryos after being explanted for 2 days; the eyes without lenses developed into a mass of retinal cells with an internal cavity, and the surface layer developed pigment epithelium when it was surrounded by mesenchyme (Fig. 49). By contrast the eight eyes which contained lens-ectoderm were all characterized by their well marked cup shape. In three cases in which the pendants of ectoderm attached to the lens were small and did not disturb its attachment to the edges of the pupil, the eye became exaggeratedly cup-shaped. This is usually the case in explants with lenses developing in in the body cavity (Chapter IV, section 2), or when surrounded by mesenchyme (Fig. 51). If the pendants are large or fuse with the surface ectoderm the cup shape is not fully achieved. When these pendants become attached to the surface ectoderm an intricate chain (Fig. 52) involving surface ectoderm, pendant, epithelium and lens nucleus arises. The lens nucleus is buried in the thickness of the retina, which is barely cupped. In axolotls, the visual outgrowths on the retinal surface facing the body cavity did not develop, in spite of the long duration of the culture period. The development of axolotl eye rudiments implanted into embryos thus proceeds as it does in saline, and when the connexions with the lens-ectoderm are kept, the cup is well developed.

The *R. arvalis* eyes without lenses also develop as they do in saline. When a narrow invagination develops in the thickness of the retina, as it does in some eyes which are developing in the body cavity, the retinal layer concentrates around it, and the surface of the eye becomes covered with rods and cones (Fig. 46); the same is true of toad eye rudiments developing in the body cavity (Fig. 36). If the previously explanted eyes develop in mesenchyme they keep this same structure, but an outer layer of pigment epithelium is developed (Fig. 53). In two cases a lens developed secondarily from the ectoderm, a small invagination was associated with it and the retinal layers up to the crescent shaped cavity were normally orientated with respect to the invagination.

In grafts of eye rudiments, with lenses, from *Rana arvalis* and *Rana ridibunda*, the retinal layers are normally orientated towards the lens (Fig. 54). But if, as is usual when such rudiments develop in the body cavity, only a lens nucleus develops, this lens nucleus lies embedded deeply in the retina and then fails to evoke normal cupping. This is true also of axolotls (Fig. 52).

In newts all the eye rudiments were explanted and grafted without lens-ectoderm. Eight of them came into contact with ectoderm, a lens developed, and the retina became orientated towards it (Fig. 48). A similar orientation and a slight hollowing were also found in an eye fixed shortly after grafting. But in three cases the eye lay in the body cavity and a lens developed beside it, evidently from eye material; here the lens nucleus became buried in the thickness of the retina, and, as in other cases, had no effect on the structure of the eye.

The Influence of Lens-Forming Material on the Origin of the Cup Shape

This influence which has been examined in earlier experiments, varies from species to species. Among urodeles it is least marked in newts, and in this group the capacity of the eye rudiment to become cup-shaped is very feeble, and lenses are easily induced from the ectoderm by the eye rudiment, or develop from the rudiment itself. Even when the lens is present the eyes are often not cupped. The influence of lenses was more marked in axolotls; where the lens-forming material, and the lens which develops from it is present, a cup shape is always developed; but when the lens was absent, it only occurred in 28 per cent of the directly grafted eyes. When cupped lens-free eyes developed in axolotls, the invagination was always turned towards a substrate, such as ectoderm, endoderm, head muscle etc., and the eye was surrounded by mesenchyme. In anurans, all the eyes with lenses became cupped, but the lens-free eyes occasionally formed an invagination: it developed more often in *Rana arvalis* than in *Bufo viridis*, and was shaped like a narrow pipe, embedded in the retina.

Conditions Affecting the Origin and Disappearance of the Basal Sheet

The results of these experiments confirm the suggestion that there are two phases in the influence of the lens-ectoderm on the formation of the eye. In the first phase it leads to the formation of the basal sheet

on the surface of the retina. This membrane can actually be seen
in all the lens-free eyes which have been fixed sufficiently early,
before the retina has separated into layers. It forms in the area where
they are attached to the ectoderm (Figs. 27, 59, 61), to the pronephros (Fig. 40), etc. and is absent if the retinal layers have already
formed. Correspondingly it remains on the surface of the inner layer
of the unstratified iris while disappearing from the surface of the bottom
of the retina (Figs. 1 A, 39). When the lens separates from the centre
of the retina, the threads are stretched and ruptured (Figs. 27, 40).
These threads stain the same colour as the threads which unite the iris
to the lens. It seems likely therefore that the material of the basal
sheet at first attaches the lens to the retina, and later persists in the
form of threads. Since the basal sheet is also found in older eyes,
if the retina is still undifferentiated into layers (Fig. 40) it seems
clear that its formation is a regular feature of this early stage in
the development of the retina.

The Connexions between the Eye and the Substrates, and their Influence on the Formation of the Eye

It is clear from the experiments described above that lenses do not
always affect the development of the eye. If for any reason only the
lens nucleus arises, it sticks to the retina and becomes deeply embedded
in it, and cupping does not occur at this place, although the retinal
layers become orientated towards it.

In other instances the presence of the lens above all affects the
scale and shape of the invagination; in the period before the onset of
the circulation, during which the primary cup shape is assumed, the
normal retina exactly embraces the lens. If there is no lens, the retina
becomes tubular, or almost flat. The close attachment between lens
and the bottom of the retina can, however, lead to exaggerated
cupping if it is not hindered at any point, as for example when development occurs in a fluid environment. In order for the typical cup
shape to be kept the connexions of the lens with ectoderm and
retina must disintegrate simultaneously. If the lens does not separate
from the ectoderm, or other substrate, it will be pulled away from
the eye, whose shape will change in a manner determined by the place
at which the lens happens to be attached to the retina at this time.
Thus either the edges of the retina are drawn out (Fig. 56) or the
lens, in emerging from the pupil, drags the centre of the retina behind
it (Figs. 27A, 62 c).

The Influence of the Connexions between the Eye Rudiment and the Mesenchyme on the Degree of Development reached by the Pigment Epithelium and on the Shape of the Retina

All that has been already described, including the influence of the mesenchyme on the formation of the pigment epithelium applies equally well to the experiments using eye rudiments of *Pelobates*. In many cases, when the eye comes into contact with the endoderm well developed cartilage (Fig. 42) forms beside the eye. It is also known that the ectomesenchyme only becomes cartilaginous on contact with endoderm (Balinsky, 1939; Hörstadius and Sellman, 1946; Hörstadius, 1950; Okada and Ichikawa, 1956). It seems likely, therefore, that this cartilage and a considerable part of the surrounding mesenchyme originate in the grafted eye rudiment itself, as was suggested by earlier evidence in Chapters II, section 2, and III, section 2. Such cartilage never formed in the body region around the eyes which were explanted before grafting, and from which wandering cells emerged.

The extent of the influence of the mesenchyme on the development of the pigment epithelium in these experiments reveals a strong connexion between it and and the degree of progress towards a completed cup shape. In the most noticeably cupped eyes, which lie in mesenchyme surroundings, the whole outer wall develops into pigment epithelium (Figs. 39, 42, 48, 51, 58, 62c, 63), while in the non-cupped eyes it develops only in patches or not at all (Figs. 41, 52, 61). Thus the constancy of behaviour discovered in explants is also found in the behaviour of grafts in embryos; the influence of the mesenchyme depends on the extent of cupping in the eye, and its influence increases as the cup shape becomes more complete. Unlike the explanted eyes, grafted eyes, and particularly those grafted into whole embryos, do develop a cavity. A second stage in the development of the cup shape of the eye now begins, during the course of which it enlarges noticeably. The results of grafting eye rudiments into whole embryos and hemi-embryos confirm and complement the experiments with explants. The presence of a lens leads to the formation of the cup shape; in the absence of a lens only a small percentage become cup shaped, and then the form is atypical and poorly developed. The results support the conclusion that the attachments between lens, ectoderm and eye control the rolling up of the retina into a cup, and that the temporary existence of the basal sheet membrane is confined to the period before the retina becomes separated into layers. They also confirm that when the eye is surrounded by mesenchyme the rolling up of the eye into a cup shape assists pigment epithelium to develop from its outer surface.

5. The Development of the Basal and Apical Parts of Eye Rudiments in Whole Embryos

In order to discover how much the development of invagination in the eye rudiment depends on the peculiar properties of apical (i.e. distal) parts, experiments were designed in which the apical

FIG. 62. A—External view of *Pelobates* larva. The apical part of an eye rudiment has been grafted into its right side, and the basal part into its left. B—The basal part has developed into a shapeless retina, with no cup form, covered with pigment epithelium. The retina merges into the brain pendant. C—The apical half has formed a cup-like retina. A deep split has developed at the point where the retina is attached to the lens. The retina has differentiated into layers with visual cells. The pigment epithelium is covered by a mesenchyme coat, in which erythrocytes can be seen. Shown 6 days after operation.

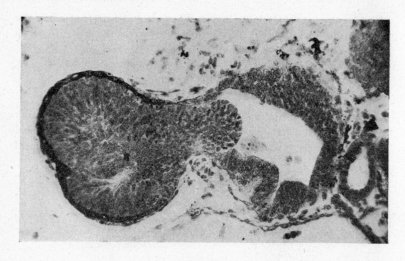

Fig. 62 b.

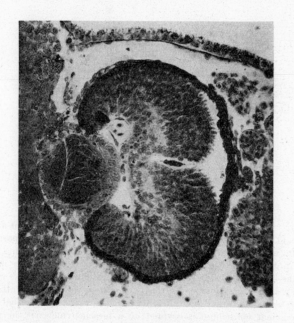

Fig. 62 c.

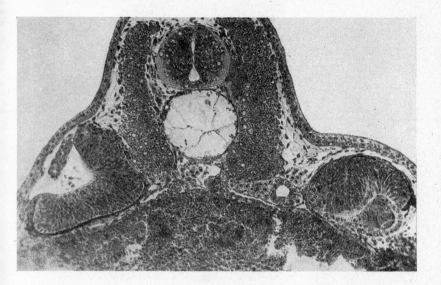

FIG. 63. Basal part (left) and apical part (right) of eye rudiment of
R. esculenta grafted into an embryo, shown 6 days after grafting. The
basal part is turned to the ectoderm and has become cupped; the apical
part with the lens has developed in the same way. Both parts are covered
by mesenchyme and pigment epithelium.

and basal (i.e. proximal) parts were separated, and then grafted
into either side of the same embryo. These experiments were also
meant to discover the cause of any invagination which occurs in
the basal parts, and whether the brain pendant arises in both parts
of the separated eye, or only in the basal half. The experiments
used *Pelobates* and *Rana esculenta*, and there were some differences
in technique. Lens-forming material was not removed from the
apical parts.

In *Pelobates* the eye rudiment separates from the brain at the very
early tail bud stage (Fig. 64, a, b) when its contour is only just raised
above the surface of the brain, and there is a slight depression in
the centre of the outer side, and a well marked pit on the inner side
(Fig. 64, c–g). The rudiment was divided by a transverse cut into
inner and outer parts. The whole outer layer came into the outer
part, including the bottom of the inner invagination; and the inner
piece included the ring-like basal part of the rudiment. Nine embryos

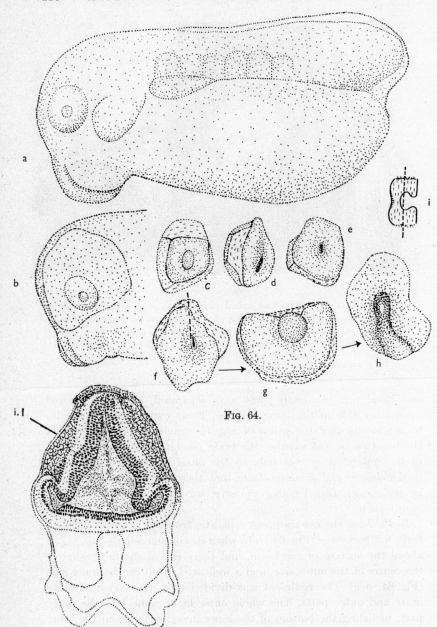

FIG. 64.

were fixed after they had lived 6 days: in one of them, the apical part separated in the form of a small explant, and was lost (cf. other experiments on *Pelobates* in Chapter IV, section 4). The differences between the transplants can be made out in living larvae (Fig. 62, A).

In *Rana esculenta* the operations were performed at a rather earlier stage, and before there was any sign of a tail bud (Fig. 65). The central depression is not visible from outside; internally there is a concavity, but no deep pit as there is in *Pelobates* at the time of operation. After the eye has been cut away from the brain (Fig. 65, d) cross section shows that it consists of two easily separable layers, which represent both the apical and basal parts. Out of eight embryos fixed at this time, only the apical parts were retained in two. Further structural details of the eye rudiment at the time of operation are given in Chapter IV, section 6.

The experimental results are shown in Table 12, in the form of a comparison between the basal and apical halves of a rudiment. Fifteen out of sixteen apical halves of both species had lenses, and these are found irrespective of contacts between eye and ectoderm; in the basal halves, lenses were found in only three cases, all at the point of contact between the eye and the ectoderm. These lenses are smaller than either those of the host, or of the apical half, are in a

FIG. 64. Analysis of the structure of *Pelobates* eye rudiment. a – general view of embryo; b – view of head of same age from which the ectoderm has been removed; a slight depression can be seen in the apex of the eye rudiment; c–e – the eye rudiment cut away from the brain of the embryo. c – external view, with flat invagination; d – lateral view, external and internal lining of red colour, intermediate layer (shown by dashes) pale grey; e – internal aspect; a narrow opening can be seen, leading into the primary cavity of the eye rudiment; f – view of the same excised eye rudiment from inside, the cut shown by dotted line; g – after cutting the wall of the rudiment; the rudiment has unrolled, and the flat, sharply defined bottom of the primary cavity is becoming visible; h – view of the same eye from outside, after the wall has been cut; it has rolled up and acquired an elongate cup shape characteristic of the older eye rudiment; i – diagram of the eye rudiment, excised from the brain (from the side); a dotted line indicates how the basal is separated from the apical part in experiments in which they are grafted separately; j – cross sec- tion of head of embryo (seen from behind towards the front part of the head); the eyes and brain are noticeably pigmented. The outer layer of ectoderm has been removed from the left of the head, and from underneath the inner layer (i.l.) after fixation all the mesenchyme was removed. This makes it easier to see the morphological individuality of this layer, which is not shown on the right side of the head.

very early stage of differentiation, and have certainly developed from the ectoderm of the host. In *Pelobates* lenses in apical halves are remarkable for their large size, as was noted earlier in Chapter IV, section 4. They are disproportionately large in comparison with the reduced size of the apical eyes. In *Rana esculenta*, however, this is not the case.

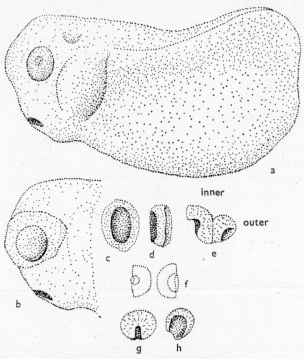

FIG. 65. Analysis of structure of eye rudiment of embryo of *Rana esculenta*. a — general view of embryo; b — view of head of embryo of same age, with ectoderm removed; c — eye rudiment cut away from brain seen from inside; d — the same, from the side (on the right is the outer layer of the eye); e — partial separation of inner and outer retinal layers; they are rolling up—particularly the outer layer; f — diagram of structure of inner and outer layers of eye rudiment after separation; g, h — surface view of inner and outer layer of eye after separation; radial lines of tension produced by the rolling up can be seen in the outer layer.

Brain pendants are found in all the basal halves of both species: twelve of them were large and three medium sized. As regards the apical halves, in ten of them there were no pendants, in five they were small and in one medium-sized. This shows that the brain can develop

TABLE 12

*Differences in the Development of Basal and Apical Parts
of Early Eye Rudiment*

	Basal Part				Apical Part			
Cup-shaped	Connexion with ectoderm	Lens	Brain pendant	No. of experiment	Cup-shaped	Connexion with ectoderm	Lens	Brain pendant
				Pelobates				
−	−	−	+>	E 798e	−*	ect. tie	+>	−
−	−	−	+	E 798m	+	−	+>	<+
<+	+	<+2ndry	+>	E 798n	+	+	+>	−
<+	−	−	+>	E 798o	+	−	+>	<+
+	−	−	+	E 798p	+	ect. tie	+>	−
−	−	−	+>	E 798r	+	−	+>	+
−	−	−	+>	E 798s	+	ect. tie	+>	−
</2/	−	−	+>	E 798t	+	−	+	−
+	+	<+2ndry	+>	E 798i				
				Rana esculenta				
<+	−	−	+>	E 802a	+>	−	+	<+
<+	+	<+2ndry	+	E 802d	+	−	−	−
+	+	−	+>	E 802f	+	−	+	−
−	−	−	+>	E 802g	−	−	+	,<+
+	+	−	+>	E 802h	+	−	+	−
+	+	−	+>	E 802i	+	−	+	<+
				E 802c	+	−	+	−
				E 802e	+/2/	+	+	−

Key: < = weak or small; > = strong or large; 2ndry = secondary lens developed from ectoderm; ect. tie = ectodermal connexions approach the lens. * = in the body cavity. Illustrations are given of the cases which are underlined.

from the apical part, but its capacity to become isolated and the scale upon which it forms increases from the apex to the base, and in this respect the species do not differ.

The shape of the eyes formed by the apical parts differs greatly from those developed from basal parts. In *Pelobates* all the eyes which developed from the apex were cupped—except one, which fell into the body cavity; the lens of this eye lay outside the body cavity and was associated with the ectoderm. The appearance of these eyes is shown in Figs. 58 and 62c.

9*

With one exception, the corresponding basal parts were shapeless and in particular lacked a cup shape, unless they were attached to the ectoderm (Fig. 62,B). Where the eye was in contact with the ectoderm the lenses which developed were marked by differences in the early stages of differentiation; they filled the invagination which formed in the retina.

In one of the eyes which developed from the apical halves the lens was tightly stuck to the ectoderm; but in three others, where the lens was separated by a considerable space from the host's ectoderm, it was joined to it by ectodermal strands. The appearance of these strands shows how active the processes are which unite the lens, which has already been laid down, with the ectoderm in the early stages of their development.

In *Rana esculenta* all the eyes from the apical halves are cup shaped (Fig. 63), and in one, where the lens faced into the body a secondary, well marked, and slightly cupped retina developed on the surface of the eye which lay next to the ectoderm. The majority of the eyes from the basal part faced the ectoderm, all were cup-shaped, even though three lacked lenses (Fig. 63). Of the two eyes which were not connected to the ectoderm, one had a very slight invagination, and the other was a misshapen tube, similar to that shown in Fig. 62,B. Differences between the cup shape formed by a basal or apical part can also be clearly followed in *Rana esculenta*. The reaction of the eye to the influence of the ectoderm, which leads to the development of the cup, is very marked in this species.

These experiments clearly show that the factors which are responsible for the cup shape reside only in the apical part of the eye, where the lens-forming material is left, or, in other experiments, where traces of its influence are kept in the form of the basal sheet. In the eyes from the basal parts the cup shape does not develop unless they are attached to the ectoderm. The retina which appears in the misshapen basal eyes evidently develops under the influence of the crowded conditions, not enhanced by the stretching effect of the basal sheet. Thus in one way or another, ectodermal connexions seem essential for the formation of the retina and of its cup shape, although the retina can also arise in conditions which only provide crowding of the eye cells.

6. On the Significance of the Connexions Between Ectoderm, Lens and Retina in the Normal Formation of the Eye Rudiment

In concluding this chapter, it is important to estimate the value of these regularities in normal eye development. The usual methods, including the dissection of living embryos, were employed to trace the changes which occur in the relations of ectoderm, eye rudiment and lens during development, and to follow how the capacity of the eye rudiment to roll up varies with the changes which take place during development in the different species. Observations were made on *Pelobates*, axolotls, *Rana arvalis* and *Rana esculenta*. Separate additional data were obtained from other species. Tables 8 and 9 show the data from *Pelobates* and axolotl.

The earliest stage examined was the early tail bud stage in *Pelobates* (Fig. 64, a). In this species, unlike any other amphibian used in these experiments, the fins are already well defined by this stage. The outer layer of ectoderm can be removed from the head very easily. The large eye rudiment appears as an evagination from the brain wall; in the middle of the exposed eye rudiment is a small, very shallow, clearly defined invagination (Fig. 64, b).

The structure of the eye rudiment is clearly visible when the rudiment is cut away from the brain (Fig. 64, c, d, e). The inside and outside surfaces are covered by a pale red coloured layer, and between them lies a mass of pale grey substance (Fig. 64, d). The inward opening of the invagination on the inner wall (Fig. 64, e, f) corresponds to the depression on the outer wall (Fig. 64, c). When the edge of this opening is cut through, the bottom of the internal invagination can be seen as a clearly defined circular flattening, separated from the side walls (Fig. 64, g). It corresponds in position to the depression on the outer surface of the eye. The arrangement shown in Fig. 64, g did not last more than a few minutes; the eye rudiment begins to curl up fairly quickly around the depression on the outer surface, and by so doing acquires the shape of a depression, elongated along the dorso-ventral axis (Fig. 64, h). This, of course, occurs when the apical and basal parts of the rudiment are separated from each other; but if the outer surface layer, including the area of the external depression, is carefully taken off, this rolling up does not occur. In order to show exactly what happens to the inner ectoderm layer, sections were made of embryos from which the outer layer of the ectoderm had been removed, and the mesenchyme taken away. Cross sections (Fig. 64, j) showed that the inner layer of the ectoderm remained in the eye rudiment in the form of a very thin sheath, and this is confirmed by the experiments with grafts of apical and basal parts of rudiments, described in Chapter IV, section 5. The fact that the eye rudiment does not roll up when its surface layer has been removed shows how important this layer is for the mechanics of the process: this was also shown when eye rudiments were explanted with lens material (Chapter IV, section 2).

Results from the later stages (Table 9, b, c) show that while the lens rudiment is thickening it stays closely attached to the bottom of the invaginating retina, and at the same time, tightly united to the ectoderm. At the start of this period, faint radial striations reflecting the developing lines of tension can be seen on the exposed eye rudiment. Still later, after circulation has started, the lens separates from the bottom of the retina, and from the ectoderm immediately afterwards, and all that remains of the earlier connexions is thread-like strands between the lens and the edge of part of the inner surface of the iris. At the same time a continuous mesenchyme coat develops around the neural parts of the eye and lens and this forms a new mechanical system to take part in the formation of the eye. The formation of layers in the retina begins immediately after the events just described.

Similar results were obtained from corresponding observations on the eye rudiments of *Rana esculenta*. Somewhat younger stages were examined than in *Pelobates*, and the eye rudiments were also operated on earlier (Chapter IV, section 5). When the outer ectoderm is removed at the stage shown in Fig. 65a, there is still no marked depression in the middle of the eye rudiment (Fig. 65, b). When the rudiment is excised from the wall of the brain, the concavity can be seen from the inner side (Fig. 65, c, d). The rudiment can easily be separated into outer and inner layers: apart from the material of the eye rudiment, the outer layer also includes cells of the inner ectoderm layer. This observation is confirmed by the experiments on separate grafts of these layers, described in Chapter IV, section 5.

As the layers of the eye rudiment are separated, the outer layer— which has so far been convex—immediately begins to curl up and acquire a cup-shape; the concavity of the separated inner layer is only slightly accentuated (Fig. 65, e, f, g, h). Characteristic radial striations appear along the outer edge of the invagination (Fig. 65, h). When the layers are separated at an earlier stage, there is less curling up of the outer layer. Slightly later, in the early tail bud stage, a slight cavity can be seen in the centre of the exposed eye rudiment and this is found in *Pelobates* of the same age. The curling up of the separated outer layer is even more marked. Both in *Rana esculenta* and in *Pelobates*, at a still later stage (stage 18) when the eye is a flattened cup, the flat lens rudiment sticks both to the eye and to the ectoderm; at this time, the edges of the eye rudiment are also stuck to the ectoderm.

When the lens is removed, and the mesenchyme coat and pigment epithelium are peeled off at a later stage, after the circulation has started, the eye rudiment curls up even more, and the eye fissure dilates. This indicates that at this stage, while the lens is still closely attached to the ectoderm, it has a largely restraining function which prevents excessive curling. In *R. esculenta*, the lens becomes isolated from the ectoderm and leaves the bottom of the retina very soon after circulation has begun.

In *Rana arvalis*, the changes which take place during the development of the eye differ very little from those in other species, except that at the stage when the neural folds are meeting, the lens-forming layer of the inner ectoderm comes away even more easily from the eye rudiment; histological sections of "cleaned" eyes at this stage, and data from explants and grafts from eye rudiments of this species also confirm this point. The results from later stages correspond to those obtained from *Rana esculenta*.

Observations on eye rudiments of *Bufo viridis* show that while the neural folds are closing, the lens-forming layer is only feebly connected to the eye rudiment, and this is confirmed by the grafting and explanting experiments of Chapter IV, sections 2 and 4. When eye rudiments were separated into apical and ring-like basal halves, the apical part rolled up very noticeably when the lens-forming layer was left, but did not do so when it was removed.

The axolotl eye was used for urodele material (Table 8). After the closure of the neural folds (Table 8, a–c), the early stages differ from those of anurans: the walls of the vesicles are thin in comparison with the size of the cavity, and are of uniform thickness. The single layered ectoderm is hardly attached to the eye at all, and only gradually becomes so during stages 24–25. At this stage the isolated rudiment does not lose its shape, and its volume is only slightly reduced. When the apical half is separated from the basal half the shape of the former does not change, and the rolling which is characteristic of anuran eye rudiments does not occur. A small, pale-coloured patch with radially striated edges arises at this stage in the upper half of the eye where it is stuck to the ectoderm (Table 8, c). It marks the small area of attachment, and indicates that in the region of the patch, the rolling up forces are still not strong enough to roll the apex of the rudiment. The onset of its appearance varies and sometimes it is only found in the later stages (not stages 24–25 but 25–26).

The area of the attachment between the eye rudiment and the eye increases directly after this stage, and the eye itself begins to form a flat invagination (Table 8, d–f, stages 27–35). The area of the invagination at first increases, and then diminishes, relative to the area of the whole attachment between the eye and the ectoderm. All this time the arising lens, and the ectoderm into which it merges can be separated without difficulty from the invagination and from the marginal part of the eye cup, leaving in the ectoderm the characteristic attachment mark free from mesenchyme (Table 8, d). The behaviour of an isolated urodele eye rudiment in these stages differs noticeably from that of an anuran eye rudiment. If a rudiment is separated from the ectoderm in the first of these stages (Table 8, d), when the lens is still not apparent, the invagination is lost and the rudiment becomes rounded again. In the last stage (Table 8, f), when the circulation has started, the rolling up of the eye is still unstable: if the eye is separated from the ectoderm and from the lens on one side, and from the mesenchyme coat on the other, it gradually unrolls. The shape of the retina in these stages is evidently primarily maintained by its attachments to the ectoderm and lens. If the coats are cut through at the stage when the circulation is starting (Table 8, g, h) and when they are beginning to enclose the eye, the retina swells and its volume increases. This does not occur if the cut is made in the earlier stages. It seems likely that the shape and volume of the retina are beginning to be controlled by a balance between the internal pressure and the opposing restriction exerted by the coats. The lens is now easily freed from the iris; but it rapidly becomes attached to the edge of the iris and, until the iris darkens and chromatophores develop in it (Stage 40), the attachment is very durable.

Newts were not studied in great detail. At the optic vesicle stage, the walls of the eye are thinner than in axolotls, and if the eye is isolated at this stage, the configuration of the rudiment and of its parts does not alter, as it does in axolotls. This is not surprising, since of the amphibians examined, newts occupy an extreme position in respect of their morphogenetic properties.

The experimental results agree completely with those observed in normal development. In anurans the difference in the thickness of the walls of the eye rudiment is rather constant, and the cup shape develops well in the explants. Corresponding to this is the ability of the apical half of the rudiment to roll up when separated from the embryo. The mechanisms involved in rolling obviously devolop very early in anurans, but are not enough at this stage to overcome the resistance to it exerted by the other parts of the rudiment.

The lens-forming layer is at first included in this curling up system; but just as the basal sheet can develop without the layer, invagination can also arise experimentally without further contact with the ectoderm. Later, as previous evidence shows, the retina keeps its cup shape, and the developing lens restricts the scale of the invagination and helps it to acquire a definite shape. As the lens forms it attaches to the outer layer of the ectoderm and unites with the retina and, as the experiments show, both processes proceed very actively. They also show that while the lens assists the rolling of the eye into a cup shape, its opposing function, that of restricting the extent of the rolling, requires attachment to a substrate, if cupping is not to be exaggerated.

Experimental results on urodele amphibians showed that at the optic vesicle stage the difference between the presumptive layers of the eye rudiment is extremely unstable; there is little or no difference in axolotls, and even less in newts. Correspondingly no real tendency to roll up can be found in the apical half. The apical patch, which marks where the eye rudiment is stuck to the ectoderm, enlarges very slowly, and when the already flattening eye cup is separated from the ectoderm, its shape is lost. This indicates that in urodeles, the most important factor in the mechanism of rolling up is the prolonged contact with the ectoderm and the participation of the lens anlage and not, as in anurans, processes confined to the actual retinal and lens anlagen. In anurans, the presumptive lens enters very early and very closely into the structure of the eye rudiment and becomes independent of the covering ectoderm. In urodeles, the lens anlage remains for a long period as a part of the single layered ectoderm, and is feebly attached to the eye, though these attachments are later strengthened. Differences in the mechanisms of rolling correspond to these differences in the timing of the primary morphogenetic movements in the early development of the urodele and anuran eye rudiments.

The localization of the rolling mechanisms must not be oversimplified. Because rolling does not occur in the apical part of the anuran eye rudiment when the outer layer of the rudiment is removed, and the cup shape is lost if the urodele rudiment is separated from the ectoderm, it should not be assumed that the attachment between the eye and the ectoderm constitutes the whole rolling mechanism. The whole retina obviously rolls up because of the active lengthening of its polarized cells, whose pulling force is exerted against a fixed substrate. As a substrate either the area of the attachment between lens rudiment and retina or the basal sheet may be used, and the part played by the substrate varies according to the species. This constitutes the primary rolling mechanism of the eye. Later the lens becomes important by affecting the shape and size of the invagination. The extremely important growth of the retinal layer, which lies on the external surface of the cup facing the pigment epithelium, is the third factor involved. As is shown by the results described in this section, the influence of the retina on rolling up counteracts the influence of this outer layer, which by thinning out to develop into pigment epithelium assists the process of cupping. These mechanisms are only temporary, and are concerned with producing the first period in the formation of the cup shape. When the circulation starts they break down, and are superseded by a new mechanical system which supports the structure of the eye by a balance between the pressure within the eye and the restraining influence of the mesenchyme coats (Chapter III, section 6). The consistency of the retina changes, and the early attachments between ectoderm, lens and eye are now represented only by contact between the lens and the inner layer of the iris. The great importance of the simultaneous rupture of these early attachments is shown experimentally when a failure in timing leads to a breakdown in the eye structure.

Dejean's (1939), Rochon-Duvigneaud's (1943) and Romano's (1936) work on normal eye development tends to confirm the importance of the zones of attachment, and of the function of the basal sheet. Over the area where the eye rudiment is adherent to the lens-forming ectoderm, a layer develops which is distinguished in preparations by its colour. It is formed by the basal membrane of the retina and the outer membrane of the developing lens. The material which forms the layer between the lens and retina is evidently homogeneous, but when there is no lens, it is represented by the basal sheet alone. When the retina parts from the lens, the material which lies between them is distributed along the developing posterior chamber of the eye to form the beginnings of the vitreous body. Either the substance of the area of attachment between the ectoderm and the eye, or the basal sheet arising from the surface of the eye can act as a means of polarizing the retinal cells and of unifying their movements. When the retina separates into layers, and the basal sheet disintegrates, its material becomes stretched out in the form of threads; these rapidly break down, giving rise to the first element of the vitreous body. Where the basal sheet persists, however, on the surface of the internal layer of the iris which is not separating into layers, the fibres which unite the lens to the iris are retained. They are the first of the zonule fibres which unite the lens to the ciliary zone in the adult eye.

The experimental results, concerning the mechanisms of eye formation given in this chapter also agree completely with evidence from normal eye development. The ability of the retina to roll into the cup shape varies in different species: it appears very early in anurans, and is associated with the entry of the lens-forming layer into the structure of the eye, and with the early development of the basal sheet; in urodeles the rolling up of the retina depends mainly on its connexions with the ectoderm and lens, and it has little stability by itself. The attachments between ectoderm and developing lens, and lens and retina are essential, if invagination and cupping are to form correctly. The combination of these processes plays a basic part in the primary period of eye formation, up to the start of the circulation and of the formation of the enclosing mesenchyme coat; after this, the connexions between ectoderm, lens and retina break down, and the eye continues its formation under the influence of the mechanical relationships between internal eye pressure and the resistance of the mesenchyme coats to it.

CHAPTER V

Summary of Experimental Research on the Development of the Eye Rudiment, and its Relevance to General Problems of Causality in Individual Development

1. The Problems

The factual material of the experiments, and the conclusions drawn from them have been described in the foregoing chapters. It is now necessary to compare the different experiments, in order to relate these general conclusions to a series of problems concerned with eye development. A second task is to relate the regularities of eye development to the more general problems of individual development of the organism, and in particular to the problem of its causality.

2. Crowding and Dispersal of the Cells of the Eye Rudiment as a Condition of their Development into Retina or Pigment Epithelium

As was shown experimentally, the cells of the eye rudiment always develop into retina if they are crowded into a single mass in a fluid medium such as Holtfreter saline, or fluid of the brain or body cavity. But if an eye anlage is explanted with mesoderm, and covered by ectoderm, and is subjected to strong extension, either a large part or all of it will develop into pigment epithelium. Finally, if space is artificially restricted in these explants, and the cells of the eye rudiment are consequently crowded, the proportions of the eye develop normally, most of it turns into retina, and only a small amount develops into pigment epithelium and covers the surface of the retina as a thin layer.

These experiments confirm Dragomirov's conclusions (1932, 1933, 1935b, 1939) that a whole eye can develop from any part of the rudiment, and consequently that a part of the rudiment can develop into any part of the eye. But they also show that a whole eye rudiment can develop into any one of its parts. This means that the idea that a whole eye can develop from a part of its rudiment by regulation alone or by a mutual dependence between the proportions of its original parts, is an insufficient explanation. The whole normal rudiment obviously only differentiates into the typical parts of the eye under certain definite conditions. These experiments in fact show that an accumulation of cells leads to the development of retina, and a spreading out into a single layer leads to the development of pigment epithelium.

The aggregation of cells in the eye rudiment is evidently an essential factor for their development into retina: and a restriction of the space in which the rudiment is developing amid the surrounding embryonic tissue is an essential factor in producing these crowded conditions. The subcuticular areas over the whole embryo can provide such conditions, and, as was shown by results from explants and isolated heads, the most important factors are those which regulate the secretion and outflow of the fluids which form in the organism. Otherwise, as in explants of anterior part of neural plate in ectoderm, or in explants of eye rudiments in head ectoderm of the same age, the developing eye rudiment swells up, and the proportions of retina and pigment epithelium in the developing eye become abnormal. Thus the normal development of the eye rudiment is closely bound up with conditions which are part of the whole embryo. These cannot be demonstrated without excluding a series of conditions which are usually acting in normal development.

The proportions of pigment epithelium to retina are not fixed in the eye rudiment from the start, and they cannot be attributed to regulating mechanisms. They depend on the relationship between the internal pressure in the eye rudiment and the limitations of the space in which it is developing. These neither act by themselves, nor affect the eye locally, but are qualitatively correlated with each other. The positioning of the retina may also depend on conditions which lead to an overwhelming concentration of cells in one part of the rudiment, and the placing of the pigment epithelium may depend on yet other conditions. The fact that other factors exist would not, however, exclude the possibility that they take effect together with the conditions which either crowd or extend the walls of the eye rudiment.

The phenomena which have been described are obviously the most elementary morphological conditions of eye development, which are linked with interrelations between similar cells of the rudiment. The even more elementary physiological conditions which affect their relationships will be discussed later on.

3. How the Formation of the Pigment Epithelium Depends on the Influence of the Mesenchyme, the Internal Environment of the Organism, and the Stability of the Walls of the Optic Rudiment

The stretching of the cells of the eye rudiment does not by itself cause them to develop into pigment epithelium; this only occurs when the eye rudiment is surrounded by mesenchyme. There is a great deal of evidence to support this: pigment epithelium is absent from grafts in the body cavity and from explants in an ectodermal coat but lacking mesenchyme (it is also absent from parts of the eye where there is no mesenchyme). It does develop in explants when mesenchyme is present but even then the thickness of the mesenchyme layer on the surface of the eye rudiment may be extremely thin.

In order to understand the nature of the mesenchyme influence it is important to remember that pigment epithelium does not develop in every part of the rudiment where mesenchyme is found, or which is covered by it. In the freely swimming explants, in which there is less mesenchyme than normal, and where it lies at a distance from the eye rudiment, pigment epithelium first forms in the thinner parts of the eye. Even though the mesenchyme may lie close to the thicker parts, they develop into retina. So the formation of pigment epithelium can not be regarded as a simple result of the influence of the mesenchyme alone, but as a process which depends on the quantitative correlation between the strength of mesenchyme influence and the resistance of the walls of the rudiment to it.

The effect of mesenchyme on the development of the eye rudiment is shown by the thinning of the layers, the flattening of its cells and their pigmentation. A complex of mutually additive mechanisms may be hidden behind these phenomena. As in other cases where epithelial and mesenchyme tissues are combined (Holtfreter, 1934c, 1939, 1944b) the basal membranes which develop between them become semi-permeable, and this may lead to an accumulation of fluid, secreted by the epithelial tissues, within the space bounded by the membrane. This in turn leads to the formation of cavities in the epithelium. The development of similar types of membrane at the boundary between the eye rudiment and mesenchyme leads to a separation of the surface eye cells, and to their spreading out into a thin layer. This can happen if the pigment epithelium is approached by fine extracellular threads, which form a thin membrane over its surface. Grobstein's (1955b, 1956) experiments also showed that contact with extracellular threads from one tissue was sufficient to affect the course of morphogenetic processes in another; the formation of the submaxillary glands, the metanephric tubules and cartilage is all accomplished in this way and is effected through a membrane with pores of about 1 μ diameter, through which pass the protein-polysaccharide substances formed by the cells which take part in the formation of the membrane.

The action of the mesenchyme in thinning the wall of the eye rudiment is only one of its effects: it also suppresses the multiplication of cells in adjacent layers, as Takaya (1956) demonstrated in the brain anlage. When there is no contact with the mesenchyme, as for example in fluid media, or on contact with somites, the walls of the brain in which mitosis is going on become thickened. It is perfectly possible for similar phenomena to take part in thickening the retina and thinning the pigment epithelium; numerous mitoses are found in eye rudiments developing into retina in the pericardial cavity of sturgeons, and these are not found in the pigment epithelium (Dabaghian, 1959). This does not exclude the possibility that the mesenchyme may be influencing the thinning and differentiation of the pigment epithelium by other means, but one is forced to conclude that one influence reinforces another, so that the suppression of mitosis assists the thinning process which is going on anyhow by virtue of other causes. Thus, mitotic activity and the extension of the cell bodies can both promote the increase of the cellular crowding which is required for the differentiation of the retina.

This explanation of the dependence of the development of pigment epithelium upon mesenchyme enables us to understand other similar phenomena. Dragomirov (1935a) found that eye rudiments grafted into the brain cavity turned into retina, except where they were attached to the roof of the brain, at which points pigment epithelium was developed. Detwiler and Van Dyke (1954) observed that in eye rudiments grafted into the body wall of an embryo, pigment epithelium developed not where the eye protruded into the body cavity, but where it lay in the thickness of the wall. Obviously, in these experiments, pigment epithelium did not develop in the fluid medium of the brain or body cavity, but appeared where the rudiment was surrounded by mesenchyme.

A comparison of the conditions under which pigment epithelium is formed shows the more general factors which these conditions have in common. The cells which are differentiating into pigment epithelium are in maximum contact with the medium which is the source of their metabolism. The mesenchyme attachments enable the cells to be stretched out into a thin layer lying against the fluid medium of the primary eye cavity, and the lymphoid internal medium of the explant. In spite of the large area of contact, this arrangement is not enough to produce full pigmentation in urodele eyes. Unlike those of anurans, urodele eyes only become fully pigmented when there is a blood supply.

On the other hand, if the cells of the eye rudiment are in direct contact with the blood, pigment granules begin to develop in them until they form a separate layer and become flattened. The explanation is probably that the blood introduces a phase of higher activity than that which develops under the influence of the lymphoid medium. This is not surprising, since the blood brings large amounts of substances required particularly by cells at early stages of their development, as well as bringing oxygen. The blood ensures a continuous renewal of the medium in which the cells live, and a rapid removal of their waste products. The lymphoid medium has the same action as the blood, but is much less effective. Thus blood can evoke pigmentation in cells which are still unflattened, and can produce full pigmentation in urodele pigment epithelium.

The questions of the part played by the relationship between the blood and the mesenchyme, and of the resistance of different parts of the eye to their influence, are bound up with questions concerning the origin, and order of formation of the mesenchyme coats. Hardly anything is known about their origin, except, as was described earlier on, that the chromatophores which form part of the coat originate in the neural crest (Barden, 1942). In grafts of axolotl eye, the sclera is only formed in places where the mesenchyme is pressed to the surface of the peritoneum, and it is absent where the eye protrudes into the body cavity (Fomin, 1948). The results of the present work give a picture of the early development of the mesenchyme coats.

Unlike the auditory capsule or parachordals which arise from mesodermal precursors (Filatov, 1927; Bedniakova, 1947 a, b) the original source of the mesenchyme coats of the eye is the neural ectomesenchyme. This follows from the observation that the structure of the coats develops correctly when ectomesenchyme alone surrounds the explanted eye rudiment, and that ectomesenchyme is the very first tissue surrounding the eye rudiment; its main source in amphibians is the neural crest (Stone, 1922, 1929; Raven, 1931;

Ichikawa, 1937; Hörstadius, 1950). If in these animals, ectomesenchyme also arises from the eye rudiment itself, as it does in man
(Bartelmez, 1954) then this source can also contribute to the develop-
of the primary mesenchyme coat. Characteristically, the neural mesenchyme cells are not adherent to the rudiment but are arranged
in a layer parallel to the eye surface, and at some distance from it
(Figs. 27, 55), and are connected to the surface of the eye by thin
extracellular fibrils; these fibrils form an extracellular, semi-permeable
layer, which presumably exerts an important effect on the segregation
of the pigment epithelium. This is the first appearance of Bruch's
boundary membrane which later forms the basis of the physiological
barrier between the inner medium of the eye and the blood system
(Palm, 1947; Wislocki and Ladman, 1955). The fact that the bodies
of the mesenchyme cells surround the eye at some distance indicates
that they have developed a negative affinity to it, in contradiction
to the assumption of Holtfreter (1939). The formation of the primary
mesenchyme eye coats resembles the mechanism which forms the
semi-permeable barrier around the capillaries of the brain; these are
surrounded by a coat which is connected only by thin threads to the
bodies of the glial astrocytes by which it is formed (Glees, 1955). At the
same time, both these cases differ from that of structures such as the
auditory capsule, whose cells are tightly stuck to the auditory vesicle.

The early formation of the mesenchyme coats is clearly shown in
the swollen explants of Fig. 27. The general importance of their appearance emerges when it is compared with that of the explants with
ectomesenchyme developing on glass (Fig. 24) and with the isolated
heads (Fig. 55) and normal embryos. In the explants adherent to glass,
the mesenchyme cells lie close to the eye, and separate cells disperse
over the pigment epithelium; but basically, the structure is the same,
and consists of a layer of cells which send out extracellular threads to
the pigment epithelium; this is also observed in the isolated heads. In
normal development, a mesenchyme net has formed around the eye
rudiment by the optic vesicle stage, but does not lie closely against
it. By the early optic cup stage, the mesenchyme coat has approached
more closely, but it is still only weakly attached, and can easily be
removed from the eye. We may assume, then, that the first period in
the development of the mesenchyme coat consists in the formation
of a primary coat of ectomesenchyme around the eye; its cells are
closely united to each other, and to the surface of the eye, by thin
extracellular threads.

The next period in the development of the coats starts after the primary coat has formed around the eye. Up to the onset of the circulation, there are neither blood cells nor vessel-forming cells in the mesenchyme coat of the normal eye. Vessel-forming cells and primary erythroblasts appear in the channels of the primary mesenchyme coat shortly after the heart has started to beat, and simultaneously with the circulation in the gills. In anurans vessel-forming cells also enter the eye cavity at this point, between the lens and the retina, and begin to form the vessels of the hyaloid blood supply, which is not present in urodeles (Rochon-Duvigneaud, 1943). After this, the vessels develop rapidly in anurans, both in the eye coats and in the eye cavity. Sections of normal eyes of hatched larvae show these relationships clearly (Fig. 1 A, 28, 57).

The vessel-forming cells evidently do not originate in the primary mesenchyme coat. This is suggested particularly by the fact that they lack the pigment which is so characteristic of the derivatives of the neural crest, from which arise all the primary chromatophores of the amphibian larva (DuShane, 1943; Lopashov, 1945 b; and Hörstadius, 1950). Later on, from the moment when they become introduced into the coat, the attachments between the coat and the eye increase considerably. The development of mesodermal derivatives in explants shows that they do not acquire a negative affinity with the eye-rudiment, and often lie closely beside it; pipe-like structures resembling vessels, which developed in explants of lateral plate surrounded by ectoderm, were formed in a series of cases (Yamada, 1940; Muchmore, 1951). It seems likely therefore that, like the blood cells, the vessel-forming cells also originate in the mesoderm. When they enter into the structure of the primary mesenchyme coat, they strengthen its attachment to the surface of the eye; as they enter, the coat closes up around the eye, and from this moment a new period begins and the primary mesenchyme coat turns into the choroid coat.

The sequence of processes described shows that the formation of the mesenchyme coat is closely associated with the segregation of the eye rudiment into pigment epithelium and retina. It was shown by earlier evidence that pigment epithelium arises where the eye rudiment is surrounded by the primary mesenchyme coat, and that the pigmentation is increased by the flow of the blood. However, vessels are also found in the secondary eye cavity, and here no pigment epithelium develops. When the stages in the formation of the eye coats are examined, it becomes clear that the segregation of the eye rudiment into pigment epithelium and retina depends not on any one influence, but on a variety of interactions which take place at different times between eye rudiment, mesenchyme and blood. When the outer wall of the eye rudiment is surrounded by mesenchyme, it thins and pigment begins to form in it; the developing pigment epithelium is thus prepared for the second period, when vessels form in the choroid coat, and blood begins to flow in them, and by so doing increases the peculiar properties which it has already begun to develop. The hyaloid blood vessels approach the retina, which has not experienced any preliminary influence from the primary ectomesenchyme coats. These vessels develop only in anurans, in which presumptive retina can by the optic vesicle stage be distinguished from presumptive pigment epithelium by its thickness and stability. The timing of the approach of mesenchyme and blood to the different parts of the eye rudiment is all important in determining the path chosen by the cells in their development into pigment epithelium and retina.

4. How Cellular Differentiation in the Eye Rudiment Depends on its Relation to the Medium and the Antagonism between Different Developmental Possibilities. On the Mechanisms of Retinal Polarization

It was suggested in the previous section that the various dependencies in the development of the pigment epithelium consist basically of changes in the relations between the cells of the rudiment and their environment. The material in these experiments makes it possible to extend this idea to other processes of differentiation in the eye rudiment, and to examine the mechanisms of the phenomena more deeply.

One of the basic conclusions which can be deduced from these experiments (Lopashov, 1945a) is that the course taken by the development of the eye cells is bound up with the internal accumulation of the products of their own activity. These products are probably substances of high molecular weight which take part in the differentiation of the eye, or are their precursors which appear in the earlier stages of eye development. Where these products are concentrated, the most complicated and specialized derivatives of the eye rudiment result—namely, the retinal cells; and where the retina is bounded by cavities which are surrounded by eye tissues on all sides, a layer of visual cells invariably arises. This suggests that the fluid in the cavity contains by-products of the eye rudiment cells which are less

10*

concentrated in the bordering cells than in the rest of the retina. Histological evidence (Chlopin, 1946; Winnikov, 1947 b) confirms that the cells of the visual layer differ from those in the remaining retinal mass, and are more like neural crest derivatives.

If the cells of the eye rudiment are arranged in a thin layer on the border between the inner eye medium and the lymphoid medium of the explant, they turn into pigment epithelium. This may be something to do with the fact that cell products cannot accumulate in the flattened cells which are bounded on all sides by a fluid medium. A similar process occurs when the surface cells of the eye rudiment itself are bathed by blood. Although the surface cells of the eye rudiment are bounded on one side by other cells, on the other side they are enveloped by fast-flowing blood, which is much richer in oxygen and fundamental organic substances (see below). The differentiation of the pigment epithelium when surrounded by mesenchyme might be conditioned not only by the flattening effect, but by a direct physiological action on the eye cells since the mesenchyme provides the original lymphoid medium of the explant, and may have an anti-mitotic influence.

When the eye rudiment develops in a fluid medium, the whole of it forms a single accumulation; no pigment epithelium appears, and the rudiment develops only into retina. Moreover, when urodele rudiments are grown in saline, the retina does not differentiate into layers; in the anuran rudiment only the surface layer which corresponds to the layer of visual cells is not developed. All the retinal layers differentiate when the rudiment is grown in the lymphoid internal medium of explants; but in urodeles the visual layer differentiates only on the surface of the inner cavity of the eye, while in anurans, this layer can also develop on the surface of the eye which is turned towards the internal milieu of explants. These differences may be caused by a greater physiological activity in the cells of anuran embryos (Wills, 1936; Kemp and Quinn; 1954); this may then increase the products of the eye rudiment cells, and assist the retina to differentiate an inner layer in a saline environment, and a visual layer when in the lymphoid medium.

The relationship with the environment is, however, certainly not restricted to these phenomena alone and the development of the rudiment probably depends more directly on the composition of the medium. Precise biochemical analysis of the medium cannot be given without special research on larval blood, lymphoid fluid, and fluid from the eye and other cavities. The data must therefore be confined to known facts, taken mainly from adult animals.

The differences in these media are as follows: the blood is made up of 40–45 per cent erythrocytes and 55–60 per cent plasma, and thanks to the high haemoglobin content of the erythrocytes it is capable of transporting oxygen. In mammals blood takes up 19–21 per cent of oxygen (w/v), in *Rana temporaria* the figure is 7·2 per cent, and in newts 4·7 per cent (Korzhuev, 1952). Both blood and plasma contain large quantities of soluble organic substances and the flow of the blood provides a comprehensive supply to the cells which compose the body, and removes their secretions. The various lymphoid and intra-ocular media are characteristically immobile, particularly under experimental conditions, and have a low oxygen capacity—it is only 0·3 per cent (w/v) in mammals. The concentration of organic matter is much greater in serum and blood plasma than in lymphoid and eye fluid (100 times more protein and 10 times more polysaccharides: Harrow and Mazur, 1955; Pirie and van Heyningen, 1956). Finally, saline and other inert media, which carry less dissolved oxygen, also contain no organic substances. The concentration of organic material is relatively much lower in amphibian embryonic plasma than in mammalian. After 14 days of development, which corresponds to the end of the cultivation period of the explants, the level of nitrogen in *Amblystoma* embryonic blood is 0·7 mg per cent, of plasma 0·07 mg per cent and of non-protein nitrogen 0·02 mg per cent; in newt embryos the corresponding figures are 0·57, 0·14 and 0·04 mg per cent. The composition of amphibian embryonic blood changes throughout development: the concentration of total nitrogen increases during embryonic and larval development, and that of nitrogen in the plasma rises slowly to increase sharply after metamorphosis; the concentration of non-protein nitrogen hardly changes (Humm, 1953). Schechtman (1952, 1955) and Nace (1953) also found that the albumin content of the blood plasma of chicks altered during the period of embryonic development. It changes regularly during amphibian development, and so does the consumption of oxygen—in mm³ O_2/mg N/hr. It increases steeply up to hatching, and the start of feeding, then sinks slowly, and again rises with metamorphosis. In every species studied, the curve of the changes is parallel, but in frog embryos and larvae, and in adult animals, and particularly in toads, the consumption of oxygen is 2–3 times higher than in urodeles (Wills, 1936; Kemp and Quinn, 1954).

When these facts are compared with the experimental data, it seems safe to assume that organic substances in the blood are essential for retinal differentiation — and not merely as a source of nourishment because in amphibians this is included in the cells. They are also essential for the differentiation of pigment epithelium, and this only develops when there is a close contact with the medium which enables the particular derivatives of the eye to be eliminated. Also, not only is a high oxygen tension not necessary in the primary stages of retinal development — though it becomes so in the later differentiated state — (Pirie and van Heyningen, 1956), but it destroys the developing retina (Lucas and Trowell, 1958). In the developing pigment epithelium on the other hand, the better the respiratory exchange, and the closer the relation of the cells to the medium, the more fully it differentiates. This is supported by Reinbold's (1954) discovery that when whole chick eye rudiments are cultivated in a mixture of saline, embryo extract and gelatine, only that part of the outer layer of the eye which is in direct contact with the air becomes pigmented, while in that part which is submerged in the medium hardly any pigment is formed. Another indication of the importance of an oxygen exchange in the differentiating pigment epithelium is the fact that already darkened larval and young tadpole epithelium extrudes its pigment granules, and turns into retina under the influence of indophenol (Stroeva, 1956a). Since indophenol is oxidized by cytochrome oxidase, it is possible that when the medium contains an unrestricted quantity of indophenol, the effect of the enzyme is checked, one of the links in the respiratory chain is broken, and the eye cells are thus prevented from retaining pigment granules. No one has so far succeeded in determining the relative importance of the effects of relations with the medium, which prevents the accumulation of the products of the inner layer of the eye, and of respiratory exchange, on the differentiation of the pigment epithelium. Special research would be needed to analyse how cellular differentiation in the rudiment is affected by separate environmental factors, and by products of cellular synthesis.

The regularities of development in eye rudiments which have been described are probably closely associated with the phenomenon of intracellular antagonism between different paths of development. A description was given earlier (Chapter III, section 6) of how pigment granules develop at first in both the retina and the pigment epithelium; the grains progressively increase in number in the pigment epithelium, and are regularly extruded from the retina. This shows that a series of phenomena is at first common to both layers of the eye rudiment: one then becomes intensified at the expense of the other, which is either suppressed or displaced. This does not only occur in the early stages of development. Pigment granules are extruded when pigment epithelium turns into retina, when it regenerates (Lopashov, 1949, 1955; Stone, 1950b), and when it is grafted into the anterior chamber of the eye, or into the position of the lens (Stone, 1950b; Sato, 1953; Reyer, 1956; Stone and Steinitz, 1957), or when whole eyes are treated with indophenol solution (Stroeva, 1956a). The reverse transformation of retina into pigment epithelium can take place until it separates into differentiating layers — in fact even while pigment granules are leaving it. The capacity of pigment epithelium to turn into retina continues much longer in amphibians; in urodeles it continues throughout life (Stone, 1950a, b) and in anurans, up to metamorphosis (Lopashov, 1949, and unpub.; Stroeva, 1956c).

It is probable that when a cellular element predominates inside the eye cells it either prevents the appearance of other elements, or limits it. Proceeding from Engelhardt's (1941) idea that functional components of cells are themselves active participants in their metabolism, it seems likely that intracellular elements characteristic of retina, or of pigment epithelium, tend to the further maintenance and growth of themselves. The other cell formations either disappear from the cells or are retained only in so far as they are necessary to maintain the cell alive. As Spiegelman (1946, 1948) demonstrated for yeast ferments, once the new cell formations have developed, they themselves can play a part in determining the direction of the cell metabolism, according to their concentration in the cell.

Protein synthesis specific to the retina probably only predominates from the time it separates into layers: before this, retinal cells only lengthen, which involves movements of the cell surfaces and their endings, as Harrison (1910), Holtfreter (1947) and Algard (1953) showed in experiments on several kinds of isolated embryonic cells. Since this phase—during which substances are accumulated which lead to the formation of the retina—corresponds to the primary state of the cells of the eye rudiment, it is likely that the prerequisites for the development of pigment granules continue to exist until the cells become filled with the new retinal structures, neurokeratin protein fibres. Since it is still not clear whether lipochondria (Güttes, 1953a, b) or some other component is the precursor of the pigment granules, it is too early to decide what substances serve this role. The domination

of the cell by pigment granules remains for a long time incomplete
during the development of pigment epithelium in amphibian eyes,
and precursors remain in the cells which can give rise to retina if the
environmental conditions are appropriately changed.

In normal development, the factors which are associated with the
separation of the eye rudiment into retina and pigment epithelium,
such as the crowding or dispersal of the cells, their relation to
the medium, and the inner cell antagonisms of differentiation, cannot
take place except in association with each other. The crowding increases the accumulation of particular cell products, and simultaneously lowers the oxygen supply; this assists the elongation of the
cells, increases crowding, and encourages them to develop into
retina by simultaneously depressing the processes which lead towards
the formation of pigment epithelium. Conversely, the stretching of
the cells prevents any accumulation of their special products, and
strengthens the uptake of oxygen, particularly when they are bathed
in the blood stream; this in turn enhances pigment formation,
and suppresses the formation of retinal cells. After one of their
components begins to predominate, the intracellular antagonisms
of differentiation lead subsequently to increases in the original
differences.

So the different processes which take part in the development of
the eye rudiment combine to increase progressively the differences
between the retina and pigment epithelium. The development of the
eye rudiment and of its parts is the result not of self-differentiation
along a prescribed path, but of a uniting of the processes which take
place in the originally similar cells according to their relationships
with each other, and with the surrounding medium.

The Polarization of the Retina

The dependence of retinal development on the environment has
a direct bearing on the mechanisms concerned in developing its
polarity. The problem remained unsolved for a long time. Fürst's (1904)
scheme which described the development of retinal cells by
successive divisions was uncritically accepted by some people as an
explanation of the origin of polarity in the retina, and of the fate
of the separate cells. Special experiments are however needed to
decide what determines the fate of each retinal layer during
development; it may be by a chain of successive divisions, or by

the conditions in which the cells exist at a particular moment, or by yet other factors.

Eakin's (1947) experiments clearly showed that the polarity of the retina depends primarily on its relations to the conditions which surround it. He turned the retina of a Californian tree frog embryo inside out at stages from the late eye cup (Stage 16) to the stage at which the larva was swimming, with external gills, and found that up to Stage 20, when the circulation began in the gills, and stratification was about to begin in the retina, the polarity can be reversed. During regeneration in newt larvae, the normal order in which the retinal layers differentiate, from the ganglion layer to the visual layer, can also be reversed, depending on the relation of the developing retina to the surrounding medium (Ikeda, 1935). This indicates that polarity is not laid down from the start, and that the fate of the cells in any part of the retina does not depend on their position in a series of cell divisions, though it may coincide with it in normal development. The present experiments throw some light on the nature of the mechanisms.

Not only a general reversal of polarity in the walls of the eye rudiment is possible; but along all the internal cavities, wherever they may develop, the surface of the retina is covered by a layer of visual cells. The most convincing demonstration of this is that when pigment epithelium segregates from the surface of a previously explanted eye rudiment, the cells which lie underneath turn into a layer of visual cells with outgrowths; also, when the cup-like cavity of the eye closes, visual outgrowths also develop on the surface of the inner iris layer. The layer of visual cells, which has been mentioned earlier, evidently develops wherever the retina is bounded by the internal medium of the eye.

In anurans, however, the grafted rudiment can also become covered by visual cells over the surface which faces the body or brain cavity. This happens only when the retina develops as a continuous layer, and when the surfaces which are covered by visual cells lie opposite the invagination; the lens may or may not be present. The more stable retinal zone of the anuran eye rudiment is a case in point, and the stability is probably associated with the early and intensive development of its basal sheet which has a polarizing as well as a tightening effect on the developing retina. Polarity in the retina obviously depends on the combined effects exerted by the basal sheet and by the formation of the cavities inside the eye on whose surfaces the visual cells are formed.

5. Interrelationships between Ectoderm, Lens and Basal Sheet in the Formation of the Retina and their Progressive Changes

Dragomirov's (1936, 1937, 1939) discovery that the ectoderm influenced the development of the eye rudiment appears at first sight as an induction of the retina by the influence of the ectoderm; but the evidence presented in Chapter IV shows that the processes involved are complex and continually changing. Where the eye rudiment touches the ectoderm, it is protected from contact with the mesenchyme, and it is envelopment by the mesenchyme coat which gives a first start to the development of pigment epithelium. The ectoderm also acts positively by helping in the tightening and accumulation of retinal cells in the areas where they are in contact, and then in the development and shaping of the retina. These processes also do not develop as a consequence of a single ectodermal influence, but as a result of a chain of events which act in close relation to structural changes, and to relationships between the eye and the lens-forming ectoderm.

The effect of the ectoderm on the origin and formation of the retina begins when the area of the presumptive retina is somewhat stabilized. The effect is principally conditioned by the formation of the basal sheet where there is an area of contact with the ectoderm, and here it tightens the developing retinal cells and helps them to roll up into a cup shape. The basal sheet stops growing when the connexions between it and the ectoderm are broken, but growth starts again if they are restored. The stability of the retinal zone varies from species to species: it is marked in anurans, slight in axolotls, and almost non-existent in newts; this is because when the basal sheet develops early, the layers of the eye reach different thicknesses after they have separated from the ectoderm, and the retina becomes markedly cup shaped. These differences are seen particularly well when the rudiment is cultured in saline. Species differences are also found in eyes implanted under the ectoderm, after they have been separated from it (Dragomirov, 1940), though Detwiler and Van Dyke (1954) found no stability in the zone of the presumptive retina in similar, very careful experiments on urodeles. The tightening of the cells by the basal sheet does not mean that their retinal properties are by now established, as is shown by the fact that they can still turn into pigment epithelium, and the layers can still turn into each other. The tightening does however create a relative stability in the cellular accumulation, and because of this, a corresponding predilection towards retinal development.

The effect of the lens on retinal development can only be considered from the time when it becomes separated from the ectoderm. Before this, we can only speak of the influence of lens-ectoderm on the formation of the basal sheet. As the lens becomes separated, the mechanical attachments between it and the ectoderm on the one hand, and between it and retina on the other, begin to add to their earlier effect. The material of the basal sheet evidently forms the attachment between lens and retina, and plays an important part in the formation of the retina. When the retinal surface which is attached to the lens tightens, it takes on the shape of the surface of the lens which is turned to it; at the same time this prolonged contact continues to strengthen the invagination process of the retina itself. If the attachments with the lens are broken, the retina develops atypically, into a tube, flat cup, etc. An attachment between the lens and retina produces the typical shape only if the lens is also attached to the ectoderm; if it is separated, the retina curls up around the lens, and takes on an exaggerated cup shape. The normal relationship is achieved when the lens, by its attachment to the ectoderm and the bottom of the retina, helps the retina to develop the cup shape, while the hold of the edge of the eye rudiment on the ectoderm prevents further excessive curling after the cup form has been completed.

The experiments also showed that, when the ectoderm was displaced so that the eye stretched, these very attachments could cause complete loss of the cup shape. This is seen particularly clearly in experiments using isolated heads of *Rana arvalis*, in which the lenses did not leave the ectoderm at the proper time. The bonds between ectoderm, lens and retina must not only arise at the proper time, but must also break down at the right moment if the eye is to develop correctly. When a lens does not develop, but contact between the ectoderm and the eye rudiment is undisturbed, then similar connexions arise between the ectoderm and the retina, which can reproduce the cup shape remarkably correctly. In the experiments described, especially those on axolotls, and in Lehmann's experiments (1934, 1936, 1945) on the suppression of the lens of *Rana fusca* by the action of chlorbutol, this is shown particularly well. A typical cup developed even when the lens was completely suppressed by chlorbutol, if the eye lay normally close to the ectoderm. If the actual attachment between the eye rudiment and the ectoderm was affected, then the eye only becomes cup shaped on the side which had kept its attachment to the ectoderm. But in newts the retina has a very limited capacity to curl when on its own. Thus if no lens is formed (as a result of oxygen deficiency or the grafting of belly ectoderm at neurula stages) the formation of the eye cup is disturbed, and the bottom of the retina bulges. This leads to complete absence of the eye cup cavity in extreme cases (Rübsaamen 1950; Reyer 1950).

The attachment of the ectoderm to the eye rudiment, and later, to the retina and lens is effected by an acellular substance, which appears as threads when stretched. In the later stages which follow its breakdown, traces of it are found in the spaces where there is no mesenchyme, between retina and lens, and lens and ectoderm, or directly between the retina and ectoderm. These spaces are filled with the vitreous body, and are covered by the inner cornea on the ectodermal side.

The experiments on newts show clearly that long ties of ectodermal material, which later disrupt, bridge the space between the ectoderm and the retina. In anurans, long ectodermal ties stretch from some distance to the lens anlage. Filatov (1924, 1925) described the formation of such ties. The order in which they develop in anurans and urodeles corresponds to pecularities in the formation of the lens; in anurans it develops from the inner friable layer of the ectoderm; this layer is at first tightly stuck to the eye rudiment, and is secondarily attached to the ectoderm. In urodeles the ectoderm is single layered and when the lens separates from it, the connexions with it remain unbroken, until its attachment to the eye rudiment develops and is gradually strengthened; the processes which secure an attachment between the lens and the eye thus play a very important part.

6. The Relations Between Separate Phenomena in the Development of the Eye, and how they Reinforce Each Other's Effects

We must now consider how far the results of this work on causal relations in eye development bear upon the general problems of causality in development. Analysis of these dependencies shows clearly that the effect of each acts on the development of the eye in close association with other conditions, and that the localization, size and pecularities of each eye part depend on the correlation of a whole complex of conditions. The action of the ectoderm on the formation of the retina depends not only on contact, but on the conditions which oblige the cells to crowd together. The actual origin of the retina is not the result of the local influence of the ectoderm on the eye rudiment. It depends on whether the accumulation of eye rudiment cells which is localized and strengthened by contact with the ectoderm arises or not, and also on whether the contact between the eye and ectoderm suppresses the processes which lead to the development of the pigment epithelium. In the same way, the mesenchyme which surrounds the eye when space is restricted, assists both the appearance of pigment epithelium and hence the rolling of the retina; if however space is not restricted, the rudiment swells and enlarges, and develops pigment epithelium instead of retina. The origin of pigment epithelium also depends not on the action of mesenchyme alone, but on the relation between its action and the resistance of the walls of the rudiment to it. The effect of the mesenchyme includes a series of further phenomena, such as changes in the relation between the cells of the eye rudiment and the medium which surrounds them, and whether or not the mesenchyme covered surface of the rudiment comes in contact with blood or lymph fluid.

These and other phenomena occur at different times and in different regions, which is important to the process of segregation in the previously homogenous cells of the rudiment. At different times, different parts of the rudiment are in contact with the ectoderm and mesenchyme, and the area of attachment in the ectoderm at first adheres to the central part of the presumptive retina, and then spreads out towards the edges. The remaining surface is covered by mesenchyme, which later penetrates into the area of the presumptive iris. Blood enters the developing choroid coat, and the cells which are the first to be surrounded by mesenchyme form the pigment epithelium since they have been prepared for the action of the blood by the influence of the mesenchyme. The cells which are last to be approached by blood and mesenchyme form the external layer of the iris. Simultaneously age changes take place in the cells of the eye, and the intensity of these changes reflects differences in their environmental conditions. Finally, when the hyaloid blood vessels reach the bottom of the anuran retina, which has not been previously prepared by the mesenchyme, the retina does not react to the influence of the blood, but continues to develop along its former course. The inner layer of the eye cup, on the other hand, develops in a different way: it differentiates into retina proper, and into the inner layer of the larval iris according to the thickness of the central and marginal parts. In this way the separate neural parts of the eye are created. Their segregation depends upon when and where the conditions for the cellular metabolism in the eye rudiment begin to operate, which are linked with the accumulation or spreading of the cells into a thin layer (Lopashov, 1956).

A comparison of separate links in the development of the eye reveals their mutual dependence; but it does not explain why development proceeds along any one particular course, and does not throw any light on the regularities which unite them. Such regularities can be revealed if all the dependencies and their manifestations are compared while they are united in the conditions of normal eye development.

One side of the eye rudiment comes into contact with the epidermis, and the other side is covered by mesenchyme. The eye rudiment cells are concentrated where they touch the ectoderm, and a thinning out process begins in the cells of the opposite layer. Since the flattening effect of the mesenchyme acts more effectively on thinner walls, the thinning in the wall of the presumptive pigment epithelium is a self-reinforcing process. A differentiation process also begins in the pigment epithelium, where it is associated with the accumulation of pigment granules. In so far as their accumulation is antagonistic to the processes which lead to retinal differentiation, this assists the cells to thin out still further, and so intensifies differentiation into pigment epithelium.

Once cells have started to accumulate in the field of the inner layer of the eye rudiment, further accumulations occur easily in this zone, and the cells proceed to develop into retina. This development is associated with an elongation of the cells, and therefore leads to an increase in the thickness and volume of the internal layer; this enhances still further the processes which stimulate the internal layer to develop into retina. Vigorous cell division in the external layer of the developing retina also helps to increase its size. The antagonistic cell processes which extrude pigment granules from the retina lead to an even more complete loss of the original similarities of the layers of the eye rudiment.

The lens develops in the ectoderm under the influence of the eye, and, as McKeehan (1954) has clearly shown, its size seems proportionate to the length of contact. In its turn, the lens-forming ectoderm helps first the accumulation of cells in the eye rudiment, and then the development of the cup shape in the growing retina. As the cup shape is formed, the developing retina stretches the pigment epithelium lying over it, and in this way helps it to thin out and differentiate. The thinning pigment epithelium in turn assists the rolling up process in the retina, and by uniting with the choroid coat and acting as an intermediate link in the apparatus which nourishes the retina, it also helps it to grow and differentiate. Being antagonistic in their differentiation, the retina and pigment epithelium in the limits of the entire eye mutually reinforce their antagonistic properties.

In this way, processes which actually exist separately, enter into relation with each other in normal development and progressively increase the differences between the parts of the eye and so build up the typical structure of the eye as a whole. Their adaptive importance lies not in their isolation, but in their combination with each other. Because of their quantitative and correlative character, the separate processes of development in the eye can be enhanced or suppressed, and are thus finally expressed as qualitatively new phenomena. Such quantitative augmentation must not be regarded as involving only growth or multiplication, but primarily a relative strengthening of particular properties within the whole linked system of phenomena. In this role they reach their extreme form, which contrasts with the spatially and qualitatively incomparably less complicated structure of the eye rudiment. The typical structure of the eye is thus achieved by the co-operation of the different developmental phenomena.

Attempts to grasp as large as possible a number of dependencies in eye development make it possible to draw conclusions about their interaction in a sort of mutual reinforcement or elimination. During the early development of the rudiment the components of the opposing types of differentiation are to be found equally in all cells, as when both layers of the optic cup at first form pigment granules which are later extruded from the retina. This is also found in other types of organogenesis. For example, heart myosin can be shown by immunological techniques to be present in all the embryonic layers of the young chick embryo, but later remains only in the heart anlage (Ebert, 1953); in the mouse embryo it is at first also found in the mesenchyme accumulations (Clayton and Feldman, 1955). This seems to be connected with the antagonisms of the different intracellular differentiations, and with the fact that the conditions of cell development strengthen some of their forms and suppress others. The concept of mutual strengthening and mutual inhibition in developmental processes is an essential link in the explanation of how the simple structure of the rudiment can be so rapidly reorganized into the complicated adaptive structure of the formed organs.

Antagonism in the development of retina and pigment epithelium must not be considered merely as a mechanism of "competition" between elements of their internal cell structures in the sense of Spiegelman (1945, 1946, 1948). The processes leading to an increase in the differences between the various parts of the eye takes place at all levels of structural complexity — in cells, groups of cells or in whole organ rudiments, and they are combined with the phenomenon of simultaneous mutual enhancement of the contrasting differentiations.

Malinovsky (1945) was the first to indicate the necessity of just a similar type of interaction for the fulfilment of the developmental processes. At the same time he opposed this type of process to the stabilizing endocrine correlations in the developed organism. In these, if one organ actuates the function of another, the reverse effect is suppressing (Zawadovsky, 1941). Processes of mutual strengthening and mutual inhibition are specific to the stages of embryonic development, and appear regularly in the mechanisms which characterize these stages. They also appear to some extent in individual dependencies, but reach full expression in the complex relations in which are embraced all the phenomena taking part in the developing rudiment.

7. Correlations in the Successive Conditions of Eye Development, and of Periods in the Development of the Organism

The research which has been described shows how one mechanism can be changed by others during the process of eye formation. Successive mechanisms also act in the same direction, so that an earlier effect is strengthened and continued. This can be seen in the successive effects of mesenchyme and blood on the development of pigment epithelium, and in the successive effects of ectoderm, lens, internal eye pressure and resistance of the eye coats on the development of the cup shape. Similar replacement of developmental mechanisms occurs at approximately the same time in the different phenomena of eye development. They are seen for instance in the differentiation of cells and in their ability to transform into each other, in the relation of the eye rudiment to its surrounding medium, and in the mechanical systems which shape the eye. It is during the same periods that changes occur in the relation of the embryo itself to the external medium, by alterations in its general physiology.

The succession of these changes becomes apparent when the development of the eye and of the embryo is compared in 3 periods. The word *period* is here used to mean a section of development within which radical changes in the whole complex of embryonic properties occur, embracing both the inter-relations of embryonic structures and the relations of the embryo with the environment (Wasnezov, 1946; Kryzhanovsky, 1949, 1950). By contrast, the word *stage* is used to mean a conventional level of development, which is designated by a number in the tables of normal development that have been prepared for many species of animals, especially amphibians (partly summarized in Rugh (1948), and in Nieuwkoop and Faber (1956). They can be used for comparison of the course of development in different individuals and in studies of the effect of temperature and other environmental variables.

The three periods are arranged as follows: (A) from the beginning to the end of neurulation, (B) from the closure of the neural tube to the onset of the circulation and (C) from the onset of the circulation to the tadpole stage. The comparisons apply generally to amphibian embryos, without any account of species peculiarities which are discussed in the next section.

A. From the Beginning to the End of Neurulation

The eye rudiment is not separated from the neural plate during this period. It is still possible for the material of the future eye rudiment to develop into other neural structures, and vice-versa (Adelmann, 1930, 1937; Alderman, 1935; Umanski, 1935). However when grafts are made into other parts of the embryo (Adelmann, 1930; Alderman, 1935; Wachter, 1953) or explants are grown in saline (Woellwarth, 1952), only the anterior section of the neural plate gives rise to an eye rudiment, which shows that it must possess special properties, or substances, which lead it to develop into an eye. At this stage the surface of the urodele embryo is covered by a thin coat (Holtfreter, 1943 a and b; 1944 a and c, 1945); in anuran embryos the two-layered ectoderm has a thin outer layer whose properties differ from those of the inner layer (Dettlaff, 1940, 1941, 1946, 1947 a), and which acts

in a similar way to the urodele surface coat. The embryonic surface
layer becomes semi-permeable, which helps to maintain the composition of the internal medium in the cavities of the embryo. This
internal medium plays an important part in development by per-
mitting the cells to interact physiologically (Holtfreter, 1943a, b,
1944a, c). In addition to the surface layer the embryo is separated
from the external medium by protective membranes which control
its exchanges with the external medium from which it takes up water
and oxygen, and which regulate the composition of the medium
beneath them. The material of the eye rudiment (and of the whole
neural plate) still lies on the surface of the embryo, and is bounded
externally by the surface layer and by perivitelline fluid, and internally by the mesoderm.

The mechanical systems which mould the material of the eye
rudiment and of the neural plate at this period are common to both;
Holtfreter (1939, 1944a, 1951) studied the system in urodeles; they
are included in the neural anlage itself. The forces which elongate the
cells of the plate are applied to the dense surface layer, which unites
them, and they therefore roll into a tube, even in explants. In the
region of the eye, the process is particularly vigorous, and the invagination is deeper here than anywhere else. The process is different
in anurans, because the external layer of the ectoderm is isolated, and
the surface layer is formed only by cells of the external layer of the
neural plate. When it is removed, the neural rudiment develops from
the inner layer of the neural plate either without any cavity at all, or
with an atypical cavity, while if the outer layer is grafted into the
ventral surface of the embryo it submerges, and forms an epithelial
vesicle containing only a few nerve cells—that is, forms the ependymal elements of the brain (Dettlaff, 1938, 1940, 1941, 1947a).

B. From the Closure of the Neural Tube to the Onset of the Circulation

The present research shows that at this period the eye rudiment
segregates from the brain and loses its capacity to turn into brain,
except for a few of its cells in which the capacity is probably lost
somewhat later. The actual cells of the eye rudiment are still inter-
changeable. Whether they turn into retina or pigment epithelium
depends on whether the conditions favour an accumulation of their
particular products, and this depends on the nature of their relation
to the medium. During this period the eye rudiment, and especially

the retina, can induce lenses in the ectoderm, and can also, in newts, form lenses itself.

The closure of the neural tube and the development of the basement membrane on the border of the ectoderm and of the developing mesenchyme lead to an increasing isolation of the internal from the outer environment of the embryo. The internal medium consists of cellular secretions, particularly from the mesenchyme. Thanks to the development of boundary membranes, specific organ media develop within the cavities of different organs, such as brain and eye. At the apical point where the surface of the eye is nearest to the external medium, it is separated from it by the ectoderm. A large part of its surface faces the organic internal media of the embryo and has characteristic relations with both the retinal and the pigment epithelium areas.

The mechanisms of the formation of the eye rudiment involve the above-mentioned systems of relations between ectoderm, lens and retina. The direction of the rolling up of the eye rudiment becomes reversed. The dense layer which formerly lay on its internal surface, arises afresh on the outer surface, at the point of contact with the ectoderm. This basal sheet as well as the area of attachment to the ectoderm, or later to the lens, acts as a zone of application for the force of the elongating retinal cells which causes the retina to roll up into a cup. This mechanical system, while shaping the eye, proceeds in the conditions of restricted space under which the eye rudiment develops. The tightening of the retinal cells is limited by how far they are able to accumulate at the point of contact with the ectoderm, and on the closeness of this contact. This complex system conditioned the first period in the formation of the eye rudiment, during which its primary cup shape is created.

C. From the Onset of the Circulation, the Formation of the Gills, and the Segregation of the Layers in the Retina

A whole complex of changes begins in the eye and the embryo during the short period which follows the start of the heart beat, and the movement of the blood. The retina segregates into layers, and, from this time, apart possibly from the inner layer of the iris which is still unstratified, it loses its capacity to induce a lens in the experiments described. It also loses the power to reverse polarity and to turn into pigment epithelium.

11*

At the same time, all the relationships of the embryo to the environment are altered, and the formation of the basement membrane, and of the separation of the internal and external media are concluded. The growth of the gills continues and when the heart begins to beat and the blood starts to circulate, the tissues are provided with an improved supply of oxygen and raw materials. The tail with fins and swimming movements develop, and the eyes begin to react to light. The mouth breaks through and active feeding becomes possible, though it actually starts rather later and marks the passage from embryo to larva.

There is a marked change in the mechanisms of eye formation; the mesenchyme coats close completely around the neural parts of the eye, and circulation is established within them. While the retina segregates into layers, the basal sheet disintegrates, and the connexions between retina, lens and ectoderm break down. Only fine a cellular threads between the lens and the inner layer of the iris remain of the links between lens and retina; these are coarser in urodeles; they prevent the dilation of the pupil as the retina grows and stretches further. The consistency of the retina alters, its mechanical toughness is reduced and in consequence it swells easily in saline.

The size increases rapidly because of increased internal eye pressure in the posterior chamber. The volume of the eye, and the dimensions of the retina, pigment epithelium and cornea are determined according to the balance between the restraining effect of the mesenchyme coats, and the pressure within (Coulombre 1956, 1957). The iris develops, and as a result of these changes, a new type of structure, the secondary cup shape, is acquired, though it does not arise if the blood supply is lacking (Fig. 57, c). Up to metamorphosis, the subsequent growth of the eye does not alter its essential and general outline, although there are changes in the structure of the iris, and detailed changes within the retina.

Comparisons and experimental data make it possible to form a series of conclusions about the relations of the successive processes to each other, and to the environmental conditions. It is certainly not accidental that the processes of development are enhanced by the action of each succeeding mechanism. It is obviously because of such an arrangement that the formation of the different structures in development cannot take place at once, and that the mechanisms of mutual strengthening cannot develop any further after a certain point has been reached. New mechanisms of organ formation appear, which can however only build on what has been previously prepared.

Upon what factor does the interrelationship of changes in the different organs depend? Is it due to a change in the relation of the whole embryo to the external environment? Here the position is evidently more complicated. It might be clarified by comparing the development of separate rudiments in relation to their environment and function. It seems that the separate processes of eye development which are characteristic of the one period can, to some extent, exist apart from the environmental conditions of the preceding period, or the actual structure of the eye is such that it can continue to develop further when the new conditions become available. The retina begins to segregate into layers and to develop visual outgrowths even when the conditions which are created by the onset of circulation are not present, but this occurs better in a lymphoid than in a saline medium. The conditions provided by a lymphoid medium, and a surrounding of mesenchyme, also prepare the pigment epithelium for the effect of the blood, which carries its development through to completion. In urodeles and anurans, the degree of differentiation which decides the transformation into the next period depends to some extent on the composition of the medium. The primary cup shape is already formed by the time the blood reaches it, and it provides the basis for the formation of the secondary cup shape. Lastly, eyes can also develop in darkness without a visual function (Baburina, 1948; Oepen, 1950), and without connexion with the brain, although a prolonged period in darkness causes partial degeneration of the retina and pigment epithelium (Ognev, 1910). Only the development of the eye in some cave animals whose eyes are evolutionarily degraded depends on illumination (Birstein, 1941). Moreover in a number of newborn mammals the eyes are shielded from the external environment by overgrowing lids. Thus the formation of an original functional structure does not require the influence of the environment to which its particular function is related, but rather an isolation from it, and the creation of separate conditions which assist development.

This is equally true of the other organogeneses studied. Here it is sufficient to mention that the anlagen of the blood vessels form over the greater part of the body, both before the blood is formed, and in its absence (Fernald, 1943; Jolly, 1944); the heart can also develop when there is no blood, and can contract outside the embryo, not only as a whole anlage (Bacon, 1945) but also when dissociated into separate cells (Cavanaugh, 1955). The gills are developed before the blood starts to circulate, and therefore before they start their respiratory function, but until the blood reaches them, they do not develop beyond the shape of unbranched outgrowths (Moser, 1940). The same is true of the alimentary tract. Thus the organ rudiments and their parts differentiate on the basis of conditions prevailing during the period which precedes the formation of structures essential for the start of the next period of development: but they may even go through the beginning of the next period in the absence of its particular environmental conditions.

We have already noted that the different dependencies which are related to each other within the eye rudiment by a sort of mutual enhancement and inhibition are also closely bound up with environmental conditions. These relations with the environment are another aspect of similar morphogenetic interactions; but here of course we are not discussing direct links with the external environment, but primarily with the internal media manufactured by the organism by reorganizing products received from the environment. This transformation is accomplished first by the apparatus which isolates the internal from the external medium, and then by processes which become increasingly complicated and many-sided during the course of development. There are at first the organs of the circulation and of respiration, and then nutrition. After the new period of development has begun, their combined activities create a new internal medium for the larva which is incomparably more physiologically active than the former lymphoid medium. Once having gone through the primary period of development away from direct relations with each other, the organs which are now united by their functions, begin to create a new internal environment, in which the blood, with its whole complex of properties, is all important. It influences the future course of differentiation of every organ, and at the same time reco-ordinates their development by properties upon which the relative growth of the organs is dependent. Twitty (1940) demonstrated this effect very clearly on the eye. Later, the endocrine factors, which act more selectively, are added to the original constitution of the blood, and it seems likely that the tissue-specific products which act in regulating the relative growth of organs are also added in the same way (Ebert, 1954; Andres, 1955; Tumanishvili, Dzhandieri and Svanidze 1956).

It is obvious that the existence of developmental periods is based immediately on the regularities controlling the relations of the preceding and subsequent developmental mechanisms. The development of organ rudiments in the embryo proceeds on the basis of their specific mechanisms, and of the internal conditions of the embryo at the corresponding period; it can reach the threshold of the next period, even without the internal conditions which characterize this new period of the embryonic organism. However, when these rudiments reach the next period of their development, they combine to create new mechanisms for the utilization of the external medium; and this is essential in order that the processes characteristic of the next period of development may take place in these organs. We can therefore assume that the result of the functioning of these organs is not only that new relations with the environment are developed, but also that the organs stimulate each other to develop along new paths.

These ideas about the effect of the mutually related mechanisms of development on subsequent periods of development have something in common with those concerning the periods of development suggested by Wasnetzov (1946) and Kryzhanovsky (1949, 1950). However, the profound correspondence found between the organization of successive stages of development in embryonic and larval fish, and the conditions in which the animals exist, described in detail by Kryzhanovsky (1949, 1950), Kryzhanovsky, Disler and Smirnova (1953), and Baburina (1949a and b, 1955, 1957) cannot be used as evidence that these conditions are the immediate cause of the appearance of the characters of given stages in development, as Kryzhanovsky (1950) and particularly Disler (1950) claim.

The conformity between the original properties of the eye anlage of a bitterling (*Acanthorhodeus*) and of its cutaneous cover (Kryzhanovsky, 1949, 1950; Baburina, 1949a and b) with the environmental conditions in the molluscan gill cavity in which it develops, or that between the respiratory apparatus of embryos and of larval fish and the oxygen content of their environment, are cases in point. They demonstrate a simple correspondence, without experimental support for the assumption that these properties depend upon the corresponding conditions, though in some cases such reactions exist as proved, for example for amphibian gills (Rübsaamen 1951). It is all the more incorrect to speak of adaptive requirement as a cause of origin in development. It seems likely that these authors have failed to distinguish between the historic or evolutionary causality of appearance of developmental events and the immediate causes of their appearance in ontogeny. But this confusion may be just as incorrect as statements about the direct influence of environmental conditions, in that evolutionary processes produce the causal mechanisms of development, but are by no means their equivalent.

The problem of the complex changes in the structure of the embryo during the developmental periods should be as precisely investigated as the other problems of the mechanics of development. Even the earlier examination of limited experimental data shows that the relation of development to the environment at each period does not allow us to think of developmental processes wholly in terms of their dependence upon environmental conditions. On the contrary, the development of the embryonic rudiments during one period prepares for the transition to the next, if only by creating new physiological relationships with the environment which at once alter the conditions of development of each one of them.

8. How the Regularities Discovered Apply to the Development of the Eye Rudiment in Other Vertebrates, and How They Vary in Different Groups

It is clear from the evidence already quoted that the regularities concerned in the development of the eye rudiment vary within the different amphibian groups. This is evidently because biological regularities are not normally expressed in exactly the same way in each vertebrate group, but appear in regularly altered patterns in different species. Comparison of established regularities in the development of different animals can reveal the more common regularities, and at the same time caution against the danger of promoting a dependence discovered in one species to the level of a general regularity. The importance of comparative research on dependencies in development was discussed especially by Schmalhausen (1938) and Filatov (1939, 1941 a and b, 1943). The present section will try to clarify how dependencies in the development of the eye rudiment vary in different vertebrates, and how far the separate dependencies in the development of amphibian eye rudiment apply to other vertebrates. It is at present not possible to compare the more complicated dependencies of eye development in the different vertebrate groups.

The fundamental difference between the regularities of development in the anuran and urodele eye rudiments is a shift in the time of onset of the phenomena taking part and an alteration in their quantitative expression. The separate phenomena are moreover not all shifted in the same sense, but their combined effects produce typical eye structures which are similar in different amphibians. It is not only separate phenomena and dependencies but whole complexes which are regularly distinct in these two groups. But the finer points of difference in this scheme have to date only been worked out in respect of a few details, chiefly in the comparison between newts, and some species of *Amblystoma*.

It is characteristic of anuran amphibians that even before the neural tube has closed the eye rudiment is stuck to the inner layer of the two-layered ectoderm; since the inner layer is only weakly attached to the outer at this time, the lens-forming part of the ectoderm enters into the structure of the eye rudiment. The basal sheet is laid down correspondingly early, and the thickness of the retinal area becomes stabilized and shows a marked capacity to develop a cup shape. Because of this, the extent to which retina can transform into pigment epithelium falls off early and abruptly in anurans. At the same time however, the ability to convert is basically kept by the retinal cells, as is shown by the transformation of the external layer of eye rudiment into pigment epithelium after 48 hours explantation if surrounded by mesenchyme coats. Anuran eye rudiments are also in normal development enveloped very early by mesenchyme, considerably thicker than it is in urodeles. It is characteristic of anurans that, for example in isolated heads and in ectoderm-mesenchyme vesicles, pigment epithelium becomes fully pigmented when surrounded by mesenchyme, even without a blood supply. All the retinal layers except the visual cells can develop when the anuran retina is grown in saline; and when it is grown in the body cavity, even the visual layer is differentiated, and faces directly into the medium of the cavity.

In urodeles on the other hand, especially in newts, the eye remains weakly attached to the single-layered ectoderm over a long period. There is a prolonged period of instability in the rolling up and tightening mechanisms of the retinal zone. The retinal invagination is formed, and maintained as long as there is a prolonged and unbroken attachment to the ectoderm. Correspondingly, the pigment epithelium develops easily from all parts of the eye rudiment. The mesenchyme reaches the eye later than in anurans, and is less thick. The pigment epithelium only becomes fully saturated with pigment granules when it is supplied with blood; no layers are formed in retinas explanted into saline, and when they are grown in the body cavity, a layer of visual cells develops only on the surface of the cavities which are surrounded on all sides by eye tissues.

Yet another related series may be added to these peculiarities of the anuran and urodele eye rudiments. The point at which the retinal zone ceases to be competent to turn into pigment epithelium is evidently established in all amphibians when the layers appear, and when the transformation into actual retina takes place. This is not because of difficulties created by the accumulation of eye rudiment cells into a thick layer but because of changes in the capacity of the actual cells. In other parts of the eye however the ability to develop into retina is kept for varying periods. In anurans the inner layer of the iris, and to a lesser extent the outer layer, can turn into retina up to metamorphosis, after which the capacity is lost (Lopashov, 1949, 1955; Sato, 1953; Stroeva, 1956c). In newts, similar reversibility exists throughout life both in the iris, and in all of the pigment epithelium (Wachs, 1920; Ikeda, 1935; Stone, 1950a and b; Stone and Steinitz, 1957; Hasegawa, 1958). In newts, a lens can also regenerate from the iris, so complete regeneration is possible from a damaged eye (Reyer, 1954). As the present work has also shown, in newts, the ability to turn into lens persists during the whole course of development in the eye rudiment. This distinguishes the eyes of newts from those of axolotls and other species of *Amblystoma*, in which there is no such ability in embryonic or larval stages, although the retina can regenerate (Reyer, 1956). In the other urodeles, such as *Hynobius*, in which retina can regenerate, the ability to regenerate a lens is confined to the embryonic stages of the eye cup. If a lens does form in anuran eye material, it does so in the early eye vesicle stage, and then only rarely (Reyer, 1954).

A summary of the most important differences between anuran and urodele amphibians can be made as follows: (a) the adherence of the eye rudiment to the ectoderm, and the differentiation of the basal sheet is achieved much earlier and more fully in anurans than in urodeles, and this produces stability in the retinal zone, (b) the anuran retina differentiates further into layers when in saline or body fluid than the urodele, (c) in the absence of a blood supply, the anuran pigment epithelium also differentiates further than in urodeles, (d) the ability of the anuran pigment epithelium and iris to turn into retina is lost at metamorphosis, while it is kept throughout life in newts, whose eye material can also transform into a lens throughout life. This shifting of phenomena into earlier stages, shown by this comparison, also leads to variations in the importance of the relation of the different anlage each to other and to the internal media of the embryo during development.

Changes of correlations in mechanisms of eye development can also be found in other vertebrates. In fish, though experimental material was available, only sturgeon embryos were examined. Coloration of the epithelium begins when the eye is surrounded by the mesenchyme coat; pigmentation increases sharply wherever vessels develop in the coat, and especially in the rapidly differentiating light sensitive spot at the posterior pole; and where there are no vessels it remains undeveloped for a long period (Baburina, 1957; Dabaghian, 1958). Grafting experiments on these eye rudiments showed that the eye layers were reversible, and that formation of the pigment epithelium depended upon its being surrounded by mesenchyme. Pigmentation was however restricted where development took place in the pericardial cavity, although the rudiment was covered by mesenchyme. It reaches the level found in those parts of normal eyes in which there are still no vessels in the mesenchyme coat. When it develops in a vascularized mesenchyme coat, the level of pigmentation is the same as that reached in normal eyes with a vascularized coat (Dabaghian, 1958). Reversibility is quickly lost in the layers, since pigment epithelium ceases to be able to transform into retina as soon as it is fully pigmented (Dabaghian, 1959, 1960). The data from teleosts are likely to be even more interesting, because of the variety of types of development, and because in many species the movement of erythrocytes is preceded by the period of lymph circulation (Kryzhansovky, 1949; Kryzhanovsky, Disler and Smirnova, 1953; Baburina, 1949a, 1950, 1955). In a series of teleost fish Kryzhanovsky (1949) observed a connexion between the first increase of pigmentation in the eye and the onset of the circulation.

In birds Dorris (1938) discovered that up to 76–80 hours of incubation cultures of chick retina could still develop into pigment epithelium in an appreciable number of cases. The reverse transformation into retina was observed by Alexander (1937), when parts of the outer layer of the early cup stage were grafted into the flank of an embryo. In the embryos of a line of creeper chickens, besides various other malformations, clumps of retinal cells were found lying in the substance of the outer pigmented layer of the eye, and particularly along the edge of the optic fissure; in these "secondary" retinas (colobomas) the visual cells are turned into the cavity between the layers of the eye. Partial retinas, such as these, usually lie opposite defects in the choroid coat, and are poorly developed when the vessels are either few or absent. If grafts of either these, or normal chick eye rudiments are made into the body cavity, clumps of cells often develop, always opposite defects in the choroid coat and sclera. It seems likely therefore, that it is the defects in the choroid coat which lead to the formation of the clumps (Gayer, 1942); thus dependencies are found in birds between the formation of pigment epithelium and its being surrounded by a mesenchyme coat. The dependence of the formation of the pigmented layer on the proximity of blood vessels is shown when eye rudiments are grafted on to the chorioallantois: if blood vessels pass through the retina, it converts into pigment epithelium along their course (Neyfakh, 1951). In cultures of eye rudiments from birds, only a slight pigmentation of the outer layer results when it is surrounded by mesenchyme alone, and pigmentation is completed only when this layer, which is covered by the mesenchyme coat, comes into contact with the air (Reinbold, 1954). Obviously, in birds as well as amphibians the mesenchyme coat controls only the first stage in the development of pigment epithelium, which acquires full and stable differentiation only after oxygen-carrying blood has filled the vessels of the coat.

In earlier stages of development not only can the layers of the eye rudiment transform into each other, but the iris margin and parts of the pigment epithelium and retina can turn into lens (van Deth, 1940; Reinbold, 1958). This capacity to form lens is lost by the fourth day of incubation (Dorris, 1938). However if dissociated cells of the retinal rudiment are allowed to re-aggregate many underdeveloped lenses (lentoids) appear in the reformed retina (Moscona, 1957).

In mammals, Stroeva (1956b, 1960) has studied the capacity of the outer layer of the eye rudiment of the rat to convert into retina, when it is cultured in the anterior chamber of the adult eye. When the rudiment is cultured without mesenchyme, at the optic vesicle or optic cup stage, it develops entirely into retina. Only those parts turn into pigment epithelium which are still covered by mesenchyme cells, or which come into contact with the iris of the host. When the mesenchyme coat is retained, the eye develops with pigment epithelium, but in nearly half the experiments on eyes of 11.5 and 12.5 day embryos retinal patches develop with it. When the rudiments were cultured with mesenchyme, at the later stage when the outer layer was beginning to be pigmented, these retinal patches developed in it much more rarely, and then only along the margin of the pupil and the embryonic fissure; but when there was no mesenchyme, every part of the outer layer turned into retina. In rudiments which were implanted 24 hours later, that is, from 14.5 day embryos, in an overwhelming number of cases normal pigment epithelium was differentiated.

Patches of retina probably form in the outer layer even when the mesenchyme coat is present, because no pressure can develop inside the eye without a blood supply; the outer layer is therefore unstretched, and this evidently leads to the formation of retinal patches in it (Stroeva, 1960). The idea that there is a connexion between internal eye pressure and retinal patches is supported by the appearance of corresponding aberrations in the eyes of embryonic rats: when pregnant females are subjected to the influence of various agents, such as irradiation, heat-shock or hypovitaminosis, the effects are always associated with a delayed closure of the eye fissure, which produces either a slight or a complete drop in the internal eye pressure (Warkany and Schraffenberger, 1946, Giroud, Delmas, Lefebvres and Prost, 1954; Giroud, 1957; Stroeva, 1960). In the same way the mammalian mesenchyme can only exert an effect when the external layer of the eye is stretched into a single-layered epithelium. It acts through the force which develops when the eye rudiment rolls into a cup, and later, after the closure of the embryonic fissure, by means of internal pressure in the eye.

These experiments throw new light on the causation of a well known congenital deformity in the eyes of domestic animals and man — colobomata of the retina and choroid coat. According to Mann (1957), and Dejean, Hervouët and Leplat (1958) the appearance of retina in the outer layer of the eye rudiment, which is characteristic of the early stage of the abnormality, is connected with an exaggerated growth of the internal layer, which causes it to envaginate outwards through the edge of the optic fissure, and thereby prevents its normal closure; the origin of this typical coloboma, does not however explain the origin of a coloboma which forms away from the marginal zone. Data quoted earlier suggest that both typical and atypical colobomata have a common cause in the ability of the external layer of the eye to turn into retina; this can happen if the mesenchyme coat is injured, or if the internal pressure in the eye is disturbed, if a normal blood supply is lacking in the rudiment, or if the fissure fails to close, and it is a capacity whose manifestation is normally concealed (Stroeva, 1960). Thus in all the vertebrates studied, a dependence was found between the formation of the pigment epithelium and the influence of the mesenchyme, and of the tension in the outer layer and the blood supply, but the relative importance of the components varies according to the species.

It is possible to find some connexion between the period at which the layers of the eye rudiment can convert into each other in different species, and the capacity of the eye to regenerate. Only urodele amphibians can regenerate as adults, and only newts can regenerate a complete eye because their pigment epithelium can not only turn into retina, as in other urodeles, but also into lens and iris. In anurans retina can develop from the pigmented layer of the eye only up to metamorphosis, and the lens cannot regenerate. Thus in all the amphibians examined, the capacity of the outer layer of the eye to turn into retina which is found in all vertebrate embryonic stages, is kept up to metamorphosis or throughout life. In other vertebrates, including fish, this conversion is possible only until the outer layer of the eye is partially or completely pigmented, or, in other words, until it acquires a specific differentiation.

It seems that the complicated and specialized visual and other organs need a long period of development; the original period during which the eye tissues are differentiated and during which the less specialized outer layer of the eye can transform into retina, is shifted in the majority of vertebrates into the early stages of development. Amphibians have a special position in the sense that this phenomenon of metaplastic reversibility is prolonged over a longer period of their life. However, such a metaplasia does not lead to a complete adaptive regeneration in all the amphibia; only in newts have special regenerative mechanisms been elaborated, which ensure a complete restoration of eye structure (Lopashov, 1959).

CHAPTER VI

Mechanisms of Development in Eye Rudiments and General Regularities of Relations between Parts in Embryonic Development

1. The Elementary Levels of Segregation in Embryos and the Simplest Mechanisms of Development in their Rudiments

Some new regularities in the development of the eye rudiment have been discovered, but data from one case of organogenesis cannot be used as a basis for general conclusions. To provide such a basis, we must also compare them with other mechanisms of development, and take into account phenomena which have not been approached during the present research.

Many types of relationship between the parts of the developing embryo have been established by experimental embryology—contact induction, "assimilatory" and gradient influence of one part on another, hormonal influences, positive or negative tissue affinities, cell movements, etc. Though these phenomena may be separately distinguished and classified, they are in fact never isolated but interact and co-operate with each other. The data on eye development (Chapter VI, section 6) and on the axial rudiment of amphibian embryos (Chapter VI, section 2) clearly illustrate this; the general tendency in all these changes is to increase specific differences between the parts of the embryo.

Our problem is to distinguish between all these different mechanisms, without going to the extremes of describing still newer types and introducing yet further sterile classifications. Since the cell is the basis of development from one generation to another, it is natural to examine the relation of these mechanisms to the cell, its constitution, and its environment. The tendency to interpret the mechanisms of development in biochemical terms is based on the need to link them to successive intra-cellular activities—activities which take place on a molecular or macromolecular scale or at the extreme, at the level of visible cellular particles.

When individual amphibian embryonic cells are isolated in saline, they differentiate up to a certain level. Neural anlage cells from neurulae develop into branched, differentiated neuroblasts, ectoderm cells into epidermal cells and mesoderm cells into myoblasts (Holtfreter 1946, 1947, 1948b). Isolated neural fold cells develop into mesenchyme, pre-chondrial and pigment cells (Twitty, 1945; Holtfreter, 1947; Niu 1947, 1954). Thus even away from the conditions provided by the developing organism, the cells do not remain in an embryonic state, but change until they approximate to one or other type of differentiated cell.

It is also true that when isolated, such cells do not develop as far as do cells growing in embryos of a corresponding age. Additions made to the environment may enable cells to develop further. Thus if coelomic fluid of an adult newt is used instead of saline, the percentage of pigment cells in cultures of newt neural folds rises steeply (Twitty 1945; Niu, 1947, 1954). In saline the cells of the head section of the folds develop as far as pre-chondrial cells of the visceral skeleton (Niu, 1947, 1954) but without certain conditions such as contact with the endoderm they cannot form cartilage (Raven, 1933; Balinsky, 1939; Hörstadius and Sellman, 1946; Hörstadius, 1950; Okada and Ichikawa, 1956, and data from Chapter IV, section 4 of the present work). Cells of the blood anlage in saline develop into moving amoeboid cells, but in coelomic fluid they form lymphocytes and erythrocytes without haemoglobin (Holtfreter, 1948b; Finnegan, 1953). The conditions required before the cells can reach a certain level vary for different cellular forms.

It is not only the actual process of differentiation that is in question but also the capacity to undertake it. This too changes with time. Explants of gastrula ectoderm in saline form only ectodermal epithelium, but if such ectoderm is grafted over the somites or head organs of an older embryo, it develops into various rudiments and tissues, depending on the area in which it is placed (Holtfreter, 1933a, 1938a). If pieces of ectoderm from an early gastrula are implanted in the same way after different times in saline, their capacity to form various rudiments changes with time just as the capacity of ectoderm from whole embryos would. At the stage when the blastopore is circular, all the basic organs, such as normal-sized eye and brain, nasal placodes, derivatives of neural folds, ear vesicle etc., develop from the transplant. They also develop at the stage when the control gastrulae has a small blastopore, though the brain and eye are often of smaller size. At the stage when the transition to neurulation begins, there is a sudden change; the brain develops in only some of the embryos, and is often reduced to a small vesicle; the eye develops in only half the grafts, and is much reduced, while the nasal placodes and ear vesicles often develop, and are not reduced in size, in contrast to the brain. Finally, at the early neurula stage of controls, eyes do not develop, brain vesicles are minute and infrequent, but ear vesicles and nasal placodes still develop in 35–40 per cent of cases; the mouth invagination, balancers and derivatives of the neural folds also develop as in the earlier stages (Holtfreter, 1938a; Gallera, 1952). The capacity of the ectoderm to develop these organs does not change simultaneously over the whole embryo, and on the abdomen, away from the neural plate, the capacity to form brain and eye is lost earlier than it is in the explants (Machemer, 1932; Gallera, 1953).

After the change during which the gastrula transforms into a neurula, the cells of the developing neural plate rudiment and of the mesoderm can develop depending on conditions into the derivatives of either of these anlagen. As soon as neurulation is completed, however, these anlagen become further subdivided into a series of particular rudiments among which the eye is included. The cells can convert into each other within the rudiment, and this convertibility persists up to the stage when the retina segregates into layers. The changes by which the successive developmental stages are reached in the eye rudiment can take place even when it is separated from the embryo, as is also the case in the ectoderm (Chapters III, section 4 and IV, section 4).

The processes of differentiation, and the changes in developmental capacity which are clearly different aspects of a single phenomenon can evidently continue in cells even after removal from the organism. Under appropriate conditions, each embryonic cell has a capacity to develop, by virtue of its structure and activity. Generally speaking, embryonic cells are those in which cellular metabolism leads to successive changes in their basic structure up to a relatively stable functional differentiation. These changes moreover, result in the series of periods which correspond to the general embryonic developmental periods (Chapter V, section 7).

What factors decide the choice of a particular cell type from within the repertoire of the main anlagen? Besides depending on the period of cellular change, they must depend on other conditions as well, for within the limit of each rudiment different cellular forms can develop. We may ask what the simplest form of these mechanisms is, and whether particular local influences have to act on a homogenous cell population before the cells can develop along any particular path.

Experiments on the eye rudiment have already shown how the development of its cells depends upon their crowding or dispersal. It depends also on their relation to the surrounding medium, and probably not only directly, but through the ability to accumulate particular products of cellular metabolism which depends on the degree of relation to the medium. The retina develops where its cell products can be accumulated, and when the relations with the medium are limited; where the relations are less restricted, cell products do not accumulate, and pigment epithelium develops. The changes in the relations of cells to each other is another aspect of changes in their relations to the environment. When conditions do not favour the accumulation of the particular products, the link with the products of other embryonic cells, such as lymph and blood, becomes correspondingly closer. At the same time, as mentioned earlier, the cells in different parts of the eye do not remain unchanged by the conditions which produce crowding or spreading out. They begin to lengthen in the retinal area, and this involves a closer crowding, which further promotes retinal development. In the area of the pigment epithelium, cells, as they flatten, come under the influence of the mesenchyme, and more into contact with the surrounding medium, and therefore shift towards developing properties of pigment epithelium. This process, which increases the differences between the parts of the eye, continues until the transition to the next period of its development involves the acquisition by the retinal cells of qualitatively new properties connected with the loss of their capacity to convert into pigment epithelium.

These very simple examples of the interrelationship between cells with each other and with the environment (Lopashov, 1945 a) are found widely distributed throughout development. The development of the embryonic disc in teleosts can be well understood from this point of view. If the posterior part of the embryonic disc of a trout is removed at the early gastrula stage, thus excising the part which gives rise to the embryonic axis, a single extraembryonic blastoderm develops, and grows round the yolk. However if the remaining part of the embryonic disc does not overgrow the yolk, but remains as a cellular accumulation, as happens when the oxygen supply is insufficient, it develops into a small, correctly shaped embryo (Luther, 1937). If the embryonic disc of a blastula is divided into four quarters, and is grafted on to the yolk sac, each part will form tissues of the axial rudiment; but in grafts taken from gastrulae at the time when the cells have begun to accumulate in the posterior part of the disc, the frequency with which an embryonic axis is formed falls proportionately as the grafts are taken from further forwards (Luther, 1936). An analysis of this phenomenon shows that the formation of the embryonic axis depends on whether or not cells can accumulate in the transplant. In *Fundulus* also, grafts of extraembryonic parts from the edge of the disc rarely form only blood cells and melanophores when grafted into the area of the embryonic sac; if even larger pieces are used, as in Luther's experiments, tissues of axial rudiment develop in 30 per cent of cases (Oppenheimer, 1938, 1949, 1953). It is clear that an accumulation of cells in the embryonic disc of fish leads them to develop into the tissues of the embryonic axial rudiment, while spreading into a single layer results in the development of an extra embryonic blastoderm.

Analogous phenomena are found in the embryonic shield of mice, and in the blastoderm of the chick embryo (Grobstein, 1952, 1955 b; Grobstein and Zwilling, 1953). The parts which later form the neural anlage, also form it when grafted into the anterior chamber of the mouse eye, or when grafted on to the chick chorio-allantois. If the tissues are cultured on a plasma clot, over which the cells wander, and the cultures are later divided into 2–16 fragments, the frequency of the formation of neural and other tissues drops, until no neural tissue is formed in the smallest pieces, which develop only skin and gut epithelium. Here too, the course of development depends on the size of the fragment, as it does in the experiments on eyes, because the accumulation of cellular derivatives must also depend on the size of the rudiment. The importance of rudiment size for the formation of the complete and complex derivatives of amphibian gastrula mesoderm is shown when varying numbers of mesoderm pieces are artificially united (Lopashov, 1935 b).

The importance of cellular crowding, or of the size of the accumulation, and of the relative isolation of cells is illustrated even more exactly by the development of separate anlagen than by these early stages. Dettlaff (1938) has shown that the development of neural tissues depends not only on the influence of the underlying mesoderm, but also on the accumulation of cells in the induced ectoderm. Denis' (1958) work supports this finding. The cells of the neural plate develop into the many-layered wall of the brain only when they are

12*

crowded; when these cells are spread out into a thin layer, they form the roof of the brain (Lopashov, 1945a; Chapter II). The actual size of the brain rudiment plays an important part in the formation of its various derivatives: the regularly organized fore-brain with sense organs develop only from the large brain rudiments which arise when gastrula ectoderm is treated with harmful solutions, but do not develop from small rudiments (Holtfreter, 1944c).

When axial mesoderm or somite material of amphibian neurulae is explanted in free swimming ectodermal vesicles, the pronephros, lateral plates and blood rudiments develop (Yamada, 1940; Muchmore, 1951). If these explants become attached to the bottom of the vessel and their mesoderm cells are in consequence crowded together, then somites and limb buds also develop (Yamada, 1940). When the mass of the axial mesoderm is progressively increased in such neurula explants, by adding from 1–10 standardized pieces, the frequency with which muscle appears increases proportionately from 1–100 per cent, and of the limb bud from 0–70 per cent; at the same time more muscle fills up the interior of the explant, and the number of limb buds increases from 0–6 (Muchmore, 1957). Filatov (1932) demonstrated convincingly the importance of the size of the limb rudiment for the onset of differentiation, and this work together with evidence already quoted, and data from Polezhaev (1938) confirms the importance of cellular crowding for the initial stages of limb development.

The effect of the interrelationships between similar cells on their fate is also well illustrated in the development of amphibian erythrocytes. In the conditions provided by a very small volume of saline, where the whole composition is conditioned by the cells of the blood rudiment, these cells turn into erythrocytes, without haemoglobin; when they are surrounded by a large volume of medium, they only develop into amoeboid cells. The percentage of cells which develops into erythrocytes with haemoglobin increases if endoderm is added to the culture (Finnegan, 1953). While it is unnecessary to consider other examples of such regularities in vertebrate development (Holtfreter, 1951; Foster, Cook and Stamas, 1956), it should be noted that when the stolon cells of the ascidian *Clavellina* are grown on a dense substrate, they regularly grow in the form of a homogeneous mesenchyme sheet without any new formations at all (Fischer, 1938); the formation of new zooids from the pieces of stolon is always preceded by an accumulation of mesenchymatous tissue in the partition of the stolon, and this has to reach a certain size before the stolon can start to regenerate (Berrill, 1951).

The importance of mutual relations between the cells of a homogeneous population for the essential processes of growth and division has to be investigated by other types of experiment. Isolated cells can grow and multiply only if the volume of the medium which surrounds them is sufficiently small for their secretions to fill or condition it (Sanford, Earle and Likely, 1948). In the same way, when isolated cells of a special type are introduced into another embryo, they will differentiate only when there is a sufficiently large accumulation of homologous tissue (Holtfreter, 1944b; Weiss and Andres, 1952; Andres, 1953). The creation by the cells themselves of local conditions which are most different from the external medium is as important for their differentiation as it is for their growth and multiplication. The significance of the size of the rudiment in development, evidently depends on these circumstances, and not on the energetic conditions as Tyler (1935) suggested.

Where it is possible for cells to accumulate substances which are associated with the first periods of cellular specialization, this accumulation leads the cells on to the most complicated differentiation possible within the limits of the given anlage. It is so in the case of the retina within the eye, the thick walls within the brain, the somites within the mesoderm. It seems likely that we are dealing here with substances which are taking part in some link in the chain of the differentiation processes. Such substances, when sufficiently concentrated within the cells, cause the change to the next level of complication in the given rudiment, when their production may be increased. The fact that a substance, or a related derivative of it, which evokes the development of bone and cartilage in adult connective tissue (Levander, 1945), induces the formation of mesoderm in the ectoderm of amphibian embryos (Toivonen, 1953, 1954) is an example of this. It is evidenced also by Niu (1958a and b), who showed that the RNA isolated from different organs, which acts apparently when combined as ribonucleoprotein, can evoke the formation of homologous rudiments from gastrula ectoderm.

Thus in the processes of embryonic development which have been described as self-differentiation, at least two basic phenomena may be distinguished: (a) even in the simplest environment the embryonic cells do not remain unchanged, and the changes occur in a few basic periods, which correspond to successive segregations of the embryonic rudiments; (b) the direction taken by development can depend on whether or not the products of cellular activity can accumulate, and this in turn is a reflection of the relations of the cells to the surrounding medium.

2. The Complex Mechanisms of the Formation of the Axial Rudiment and the Origin of Organ Rudiments in Amphibians and Fish

Though separate cells and rudiments of embryos can develop under the simplest conditions, on the basis of cytological mechanisms, it does not follow that when they are linked to other parts, they will not become dependent on them in their development. Although isolated embryonic fragments can go through important sections of development without any relation to other parts, their normal development is conditioned by interactions with the rest of the embryo, and without these relationships they would develop differently. At the same time, relations between the parts of the embryo are the means whereby each is related to the external medium. In order that the organism possessing an adaptive structure can develop, precise mechanisms are essential, and the interactions between the parts of the embryo during development are prerequisites of the segregation process.

Compared with the simpler, elementary, cellular mechanisms of development, the multicellular mechanisms of relations between its parts are more like a superstructure. At the same time they are likely to be mutually coordinated with the cellular mechanisms, so that the interrelationship between parts can develop on their foundations, and on the basis of their continuously changing relations to the medium. Without an exact understanding of the mechanisms which must develop on these foundations, the essential properties of the cellular mechanisms of development, and their consequences, cannot themselves be properly understood.

The fact that an elementary capacity to develop is found in all embryonic cells, shows that dependencies between parts of rudiments of the embryo in development should not be judged as exclusive causes of development. The development of a part is more likely to depend on these links only as far as they are essential to the origin of the basic adaptive structures of the developing organism. Analysis of the development of the eye shows very clearly that the dependencies in its development are not related to the unique influences of particular parts on others; such influences are necessary only in so far as they can lead the eye to develop in a particular direction, and are replaceable by other conditions which can lead to the same result. In normal development, these relations are such that they select one out of the developmental possibilities, still unstably expressed in the embryonic parts, and progressively increase and amplify it, while inhibiting other possibilities at the same time.

The eye provides particularly suitable material for a demonstration of these regularities, because its structure is simple, and the number of possible courses which its development may take is limited. However, before deciding whether these regularities have a general significance, and how far they can be applied, they must be compared with the regularities of other rudiments, especially of the *axial rudiment* in vertebrates, since the formation of this rudiment lies at the base of all organogenesis, including that of the eye.

During investigation of this classic object of experimental embryology, the greatest importance has been attached to the phenomenon of the induction of neural plate by mesoderm, discovered by Spemann (1924). But the analysis of the development of the retina from the eye rudiment had already shown that a complex of mutually linked phenomena lie behind such inductions (ChapterV). The period of research which followed the first work on the induction of the neural plate also showed that the development of the embryonic axis, of which the neural plate is a part, embraces a whole complex of interdependent processes (Holtfreter and Hamburger, 1955). It is therefore necessary even in the case of the embryonic axis to attempt an outline of the basic features of this complex, seen in relation to the cellular mechanisms of development. The actual term induction should be kept for local dependencies in development, and should be used in a general sense that does not imply a knowledge of what lies behind them.

The amphibian embryonic axis begins to form at gastrulation; experiments using vital dyes show how the presumptive mesoderm material, which previously lay on the surface of the embryo, creeps inside during gastrulation, and becomes arranged in a layer under the ectoderm (Vogt, 1929; Pasteels, 1940, 1942). The contact between ectoderm and mesoderm leads to the formation of a neural plate, with parallel neural folds, in the centre of the area where the layers are apposed: this is the well known phenomenon of the induction of neural plate by the mesoderm (Spemann and Mangold, 1924; Spemann, 1924, 1936; Holtfreter, 1933c; Holtfreter and Hamburger, 1955).

Contact between mesoderm and ectoderm is established during gastrulation, but the neural plate appears at the beginning of the next period (neurulation) of the formation of the embryonic axis. During this period, while the neural plate is formed and closes up, a simple segregation can be seen in the mesoderm inside the embryo. The third and longest of these main periods begins at the closure of the neural tube and ends with the onset of the circulation. During this period the brain segregates into its regions, the eyes evaginate from its anterior part, the mesoderm subdivides into its main rudiments, and the eye, nasal placode, lens, ear, and fin rudiments appear. For descriptive purposes the body of the embryo may be divided into four regions; the first is the anterior head region, with fore-brain, nasal placodes and eyes; the second consists of the posterior head region, with hind brain and auditory vesicles; the third is the trunk; the fourth is the caudal region (Lehmann, 1938, 1945; Toivonen, 1940). In order to understand the mechanisms involved in the formation of the embryonic axis it is essential to find out how they are related to the origin of the mesoderm and neural plate; then how the axis segregates into different regions, and how the organs which are adapted to the regions originate; and finally to discover how the successive changes in the mechanisms of development occur during the three basic periods of embryonic development.

Experiments with explants and grafts from early amphibian gastrulae have revealed basic differences between their regions. When ectoderm is isolated in saline, it forms pure epidermis, whether the ectoderm comes from presumptive epidermis or neural plate (Holtfreter, 1933 c, 1938 a, b and c, 1944 c, 1945). It only develops the various rudiments which normally arise from it, when it comes in contact with the internal, mesodermal parts of the embryos; as for instance, when pieces of mesoderm are placed under ectoderm, and when pieces of ectoderm are grafted over the axial mesoderm of older embryos (Spemann, 1936; Holtfreter, 1933 a, b, c, 1938 a). In this last experiment the parts of the brain and other organs which are formed correspond approximately to the level along the axis of the body into which the ectoderm was grafted. When on the other hand, mesoderm from an early gastrula is isolated in saline, not only do chorda and somites develop normally, but part of it turns into ectoderm, in which a neural plate can arise after it has been in contact with the mesoderm (Holtfreter, 1933 c, 1938 b, c, 1939). These experiments support those in which it was found that if a part of gastrula ectoderm or mesoderm was removed, the difference between them was not rigid, and within limits, one could compensate for the loss from the other (Holtfreter, 1936, 1938 b). When pieces of ectoderm are grafted into the mesoderm region of the gastrula, the grafts turn into mesoderm and acquire the properties of mesoderm (Spemann, 1936; Raven, 1938). In the amphibian embryo, therefore, the properties of the mesodermal and ectodermal zones already differ at the start of gastrulation; the mesoderm must contain substances or agents which the ectoderm lacks, and those which are associated with the formation of the neural plate make their presence felt when the mesoderm comes in contact with the ectoderm, by passing from one cell layer into the other.

Teleost embryos differ from amphibian embryos in many ways. The embryonic disc is sharply isolated from the bulky yolk, and retains no reserves of nutrients. Gastrulation and the process whereby the embryonic disc overgrows the yolk are combined. Segregation of the developing axial rudiment, subdivision of the mesoderm into noto-chord, somites, lateral plate, and the segmentation of the somites all occur gradually, by an invagination which embraces first the body, and then the tail. Vital staining has also shown which parts of the fish embryonic disc form the mesoderm, embryonic and extra-embryonic ectoderm (Pasteels, 1936, 1940: Oppenheimer, 1947). The experiments described earlier (Chapter VI, section 1) show however, that in fish the ectoderm and mesoderm zones are not clearly qualitatively different at the start of gastrulation. They arise as a result of an accumulation of the disc cells, and this begins with a concentration of the cells of the thickened edge of the disc in the centre of its posterior margin where gastrulation begins.

After it has been concentrated, and invaginated into the embryo, the material of the edge of the embryonic disc has heterogeneous effects on the parts of the embryo which border it, while the material itself turns into mesoderm. It induces the neural anlage in the outer layer of the embryo which lies above it (Luther, 1935; Oppenheimer, 1936).

In *Epiplatys* the embryo can be divided into two together with the yolk. When the lower part of the edge of the embryonic disc, i.e. the region of the tail bud, is isolated immediately after the closure of the blastopore, tail-like outgrowths develop from it. These are made up of a mass of undifferentiated epidermal-type cells, together with yellow and black chromatophores and blood islets. If the tail bud is isolated somewhat later, when the first somites have formed in the body of the embryo, a normal tail develops from it (Oppenheimer, 1938). A wave of influence which communicates the properties of the parts differentiating at the anterior end, evidently travels backwards along the axis of the body. This process may occur in the earlier stages, and thus a piece of presumptive mesoderm from the loach *Misgurnis fossilis* isolated at the stage when it is just invaginating, at the beginning of gastrulation, and grafted between the yolk and periderm, will turn not into mesoderm, but into brain with pigmented cells and fragments of visceral cartilage (Lopashov, 1944). This suggests that the wave also includes influences which communicate a capacity to turn into nerve cells, and these influences are overlapped by the factors for turning into mesoderm.

It is obvious that in fish some of the products which are derived from the cellular activities in the accumulated cells of the embryonic disc on the surface of the yolk lead to the development of mesoderm, and some to the development of neural anlage. The products form most intensively when large accumulations of cells are formed at the start of gastrulation. Small accumulations lead to the production of blood cells and chromatophores only. The products are capable of being transmitted together along the cell layer and usually outweigh the influence of the "mesodermalizing" substances with which the formation of the mesoderm is associated. When the normal sequence of relations between cells is disturbed however, cells in the accumulation can also turn into neural anlagen. The cells of such accumulations invaginated inside the embryo also exert other influences on the ectoderm cells which surround them. This is mainly shown by the transmission of neuralizing substances into the ectoderm, which responds by beginning to develop a neural anlage.

As well as differences in the primary mechanisms which produce the axial rudiment in fish and amphibians, there are phenomena in amphibians which are related to those in fish. We have already described how ectodermal grafts placed in the mesoderm area of the gastrula develop into mesoderm; but if such grafts are cut out 24 hours after grafting, but still before invagination, and are regrafted into the ectoderm area, a part of the graft will invaginate. The remaining surface portion will then turn into neural plate, either immediately, or under the influence of the mesoderm, only a small part of which has to creep under the edge of the transplant for the effect to be seen (Raven, 1938). Mesoderm from the gastrula can also turn into neural plate, if it is transplanted to the endoderm field, which suppresses its invagination (Dalcq and Lallier, 1948). It seems likely, then, that neuralizing substances as well as mesodermalizing substances may be found in amphibian mesoderm. In fish too, when ectoderm turns into mesoderm, neuralizing factors penetrate it first, and this effect is later overborne by the influence of mesodermalizing factors. The important difference between amphibians and fish is in the timing of the point at which the mesoderm becomes different from ectoderm: in amphibians this can occur right up to the start of gastrulation.

What are the mechanisms which bring about the formation of the mesodermal and neural anlagen, and are any particular substances involved? This question is inseparable from the problem of the differentiation of organs and parts in the axial rudiment; in both cases the problem is to discover how diversity develops in the gastrula mesoderm and ectoderm, which at first differ so very little from each other.

One of the techniques used to solve these problems was the isolation of the inducing substances and the study of their specificity. Soon after the discovery of neural induction, it was found that not only the mesoderm but any dead gastrula tissue, and living or dead adult tissues of many animals could evoke a neural anlage, and sometimes mesoderm too. The scale of development of induced rudiments increased up to mammals, whose tissues have the greatest inductive activity (Bautzmann, Holtfreter, Spemann and Mangold, 1932; Holtfreter, 1933b and c, 1934a, b). Obviously the inducing substances are widely distributed in adult tissues, and their differential release from the mesoderm is a specific property of the gastrula stage. Unfortunately these and other experiments gave rise to baseless speculations since refuted by further research; their main idea was that the substances are themselves non-specific, and act only as irritants, and the actual specificity of the developing formations must be a property of the reacting system of the ectoderm, or of the embryo as a whole (Weiss, 1935; Filatov, 1939; Tokin, 1943).

Somewhat later new data demonstrated that neural anlage can arise in gastrula ectoderm and when a partial cytolysis is produced. In *Amblystoma punctatum* contact of the inner surface of the ectoderm with Holtfreter solution is enough, and in other amphibians it is only necessary to make the medium slightly more acid or alkaline. In whole embryos of this species such changes do not occur, because only the outer surface of the ectoderm comes into contact with the fluid medium, and these cells are covered by a protective coat; closed ectodermal explants also develop into pure ectoderm, because the surface coat faces the surrounding medium. Isolated pieces of ectoderm develop, depending on the strength of the harmful medium, into whole sections of anterior brain, with eye rudiment and nasal placodes, accompanied by ectomesenchyme and pigment cells; or groups of nerve cells with pigment cells and mesenchyme; or mesenchyme and pigment cells alone (Holtfreter, 1944c, 1945, 1948a). These experiments help us to understand the differences in the mode of action of different inductors. Some act by injuring the cells of the gastrula ectoderm, or even by killing some of them, and thus causing the liberation of the effective substances. Others are themselves the source of such substances which then act directly upon the ectoderm cells. This is shown by the fact that the inductions produced by injury are neural and their regional character, if evident, is always fore-brain.

At the same time further information has shown that the influence of inductors could be associated with the effect of substances endowed with a certain specificity. This information was obtained after prolonged and persistent work by various groups of workers. They showed that while a variety of tissues, freshly killed by alcohol, can evoke the simultaneous formation of different parts of the axial rudiment, many tissues act far more selectively. Guinea-pig or mouse liver evoke fore-brain, with eyes and nasal placodes, almost exclusively, while kidneys of the same animals evoke spino-caudal regions, with mesoderm, and occasionally parts of hind brain, with ear vesicles (Chuang, 1939; Toivonen, 1940). Guinea-pig and rat bone marrow, which evoke the formation of bone in adult animals, contain substances which almost exclusively evoke the formation of mesodermal organs such as chorda, somites, kidneys etc. in the ectoderm of the amphibian gastrula; in some cases, only parts of a thin neural tube also develop at the tail (Toivonen, 1953, 1954, 1958; Saxen and Toivonen, 1956). These data show that there exist two main substances, with which the formation of the parts of axial rudiment is connected, as already suggested by Lehmann (1945, 1950). Eye rudiments killed by alcohol treatment which brought about the formation of forebrain with eyes in gastrula ectoderm (Lopashov, 1936, van Cleave 1938) seem to have acted as forebrain inductors.

Further data on the transformation of one inducing agent into another suggests that one of these two substances is a neutralizing one which induces forebrain structures, and that the other is a mesodermalizing one: in hindbrain and trunk-caudal inductors they are intermixed in different proportions. After short treatment with hot water (80–100°), trunk-caudal inductors transform into forebrain ones, while these latter are unchanged after such treatment (Chuang, 1940; Toivonen, 1950). Long term preservation in alcohol acts in a similar way: trunk-caudal inductors gradually lose their ability to induce notochord and somites, while the formation of neural tubes comes to prevail; after longer preservation one obtains hindbrain parts (with auditory vesicles) and, at last, only the forebrain arises (with the eyes and nasal placodes) (Yamada and Takada, 1955 a, Vahs 1957, Engländer and Johnen, 1957). After treatment with hot water or after long term preservation in alcohol bone marrow completely ceases to bring about mesoderm formation, and its effect leads only to the formation of balancers, isolated lenses and lentoids (Toivonen, 1954, Kuusi, 1957). It seems that during these changes the less stable mesodermalizing substance disappears by stages from the mixture until only neuralizing substance remains. However, after steam treatment of thin layers of bone marrow the ability to induce mesoderm is replaced by the induction of trunk-caudal, later hindbrain, and, finally anterior parts of the brian rudiment (Yamada, 1958 a, b). This indicates the possibility of transforming some agents into others, but does not rule out the fact that the main substances act in a manner which depends on their quantitative relations; this is also supported by the fact that appropriate mixtures of neuralizing and mesodermalizing inductors can cause complete axial rudiments to appear (Toivonen and Saxen, 1955). The effect of high temperature (nearly high enough to cause serious injury) on the areas of the upper blastopore lip of the early gastrula is to shift their inductions from hindbrain to forebrain structures and simultaneously to decrease their ability to develop into somites (Takaya, 1955 b). The resemblance of these changes to those brought about by temperature in foreign inductors shows the similarity between the action of these inductors and factors acting in living embryos.

It was accepted until recently that the influences leading to the formation of one or other tissue from the gastrula ectoderm can act only by means of a direct contact. When by various means the rolling up of pieces of ectoderm was prevented, while preserving the contact of the internal surface of their cells with the liquid medium, it turned out that such an effect could be caused by substances in solution as well. An inducing effect was revealed in substances that accumulate in minute volumes (10 mm³) of salt solution while pieces of the dorsal lip of gastrula blastopore, the hindpart of the neural plate, or other tissues of amphibian embryos were living in it, conditioning this solution by their secretions (Niu and Twitty, 1953; Niu, 1956). The same action is also caused by chick embryo extract and by various fractions of it (Woellwarth, 1956; Becker, Tiedemann and Tiedemann, 1959). Mesenchyme, chromatophores, myoblasts, notochord fragments, neuroblasts and brain fragments arise in these explants. The resemblance of such inductions to those occurring in normal development was stressed by the fact that in some experiments active substances were excreted by parts of early embryos.

According to Brachet's data (1950, 1952) at the late gastrula stage and at the onset of neurulation cells of the mesoderm and presumptive neural plate are joined by cytoplasmic threads along which ribonucleoproteid granules pass into the neural plate. It is likely that during cultivation of ectoderm in solutions of inducing substances protein and ribonucleoprotein macromolecules penetrate into its cells through their internal uncoated surface. The possibility of such a penetration was already suggested by Langman's experiments (1953) which showed that after cultivation of rat ovarian tissue in the blood plasma of other animals, species-specific plasma proteins preserving their antigenic specificity could be detected in the cytoplasm of the cultivated cells. The complete proof of such a transfer of molecules between cells upon induction was presented by Flickinger, Hatton and Rounds (1959) who detected, also by immunological methods, a transfer of particles during induction between the tissues of urodeles and anurans.

Attempts to isolate and determine the chemical nature of inducing substances have led recently to very precise methods of isolation from tissues and tissue extracts. These methods showed the isolated substances to possess the same action as the tissues themselves (Yamada and Takata, 1955a; Yamada, 1958a, b; Tiedemann, 1959). Biochemical analysis reveals in some cases that the substances isolated seem to be ribonucleoproteins (dorso-caudal, hind-, and forebrain inductors), and in other cases that they seem to be proteins (mesodermalizing inductors) (Yamada, 1958a, b; Tiedemann, 1959). Experiments with ribonuclease action destroying nucleic acids, and those with the trypsin and other protein-destroying enzymes (Kuusi, 1951; Yamada and Takata, 1955b; Hayasgi, 1955, 1958; Engländer and Johnen, 1957; Yamada, 1958a, b; Tiedemann, 1959) show that inducing actions are based on proteins. At some variance with this conclusion are Niu's data (1958a, b) who isolated highly-specific fractions of the ribonucleic acid from some organs. This acid (in combination with proteins) in solution resulted in the formation of rudiments of homologous organs in gastrula ectoderm. These and some other data suggest that the problem of specificity of inducing substances is not exhausted by referring them to one of the classes of chemical compounds known. The main thing shown by the investigation of inducing agents is that the phenomena of induction and the appearance of new anlagen in gastrula tissues are based on the actual transfer and action of substances possessing a certain degree of specificity and not on non-specific stimulation or activation.

In fish, the origin of neuralizing and mesodermalizing substances in the mesoderm is at first apparently connected with the accumulation of cells in the embryonic disc, but also possibly with their invagination inside the embryo during gastrulation. Experiments in which whole amphibian embryos were centrifuged at the blastula stage help us to understand the origin of the inducing substances. In these experiments both mesodermal and neural parts of the axial rudiments are formed from ventral ectoderm (Pasteels, 1948, 1953 a, b, 1954). When however, isolated pieces of ectoderm are centrifuged, such rudiments do not develop (Karasaki and Yamada, 1955); they only develop when cells accumulate under the ectoderm; this occurs mainly in anurans, in which cells can accumulate very much more easily, because the ectoderm is two-layered, and the inner layer is very friable. Obviously, in amphibians as well as fish an accumulation of ectoderm cells at the blastula stage can also lead them to develop into mesoderm and neural anlage; it is however possible that not only an accumulation of cells, but also its contact with endoderm is required. This shows that the interactions which lead to the formation of neuralizing and mesodermalizing substances have already begun by the blastula stage in amphibians, and are completed by the start of gastrulation; after this, when the ectoderm cells are injured, only neuralizing substances can be evoked.

By comparing the experiments using inducing substances with the data which were discussed earlier, some rather more general conclusions may be reached. The experiments on the effect of injury on the development of the ectoderm do not rule out the possibility that the neuralizing substances which develop in the ectoderm cells when they are partially cytolysed may in other cases enter the cells from outside. This evidently takes place in normal development. The mesodermalizing substances, on the other hand, normally arise in the actual layer in which their effects appear. However, they too can penetrate from outside into these cells under experimental conditions, and, as will be seen later, this sometimes occurs normally. It is therefore not possible to reduce to a single type every case of dependence in which similar substances are taking part. The transfer of substances from outside is only one of the ways in which their effects may be made evident, and it is therefore wiser to call them "inducing" with reservations. Their normal distribution in the embryo is evidently connected with the mechanisms which are concerned with the creation of adaptive structures in the axial rudiment. The most important aspects of the effects of such substances may be estimated as follows. First the developmental tendencies of the cells, their shape and movement start to change according to the presence of these substances just as, for example, the mesoderm cells acquire mobility, and the capacity to move inside the embryo during gastrulation. Then, when the transition to the next period of development occurs, the cells acquire properties of one cell type or another, according to the previous influence of these substances, and lose their power to convert into the cells of the remaining parts of the anlage of which they originally formed part. This is somewhat similar to the influences of substances concentrated in the accumulations of the cells which manufacture them, as for example in the retina of the eye (Chapter VI, section 1).

The data on inducing substances agree well, not only with findings described earlier, but also with the evidence on the mechanisms of regional segregation in living embryos. Naturally, these mechanisms cannot be attributed to the influence of one particular substance, but include a more involved complex of phenomena. The first experiments on the regional differentiation of the axial rudiment gave the impression that the regionality of the neural plate and ectodermal organs was an expression of primary segregation in the mesoderm (Spemann, 1931, 1936; Mangold, 1933b; Holtfreter, 1933a). Later research however showed that this differentiation was to some extent associated with processes begun in the ectoderm itself after it had come under mesodermal influence.

Mesoderm in the course of gastrulation and neurulation changes in respect of its capacity to turn into ectoderm, and the capacity of its parts to turn into each other. After gastrulation, the ability of the mesoderm to convert into ectoderm is lost. However, apart from the notochord an interchange of developmental fate can still

occur within the mesoderm itself at the neurula stage, but before
the parts of the mesoderm have become structurally different from
one another. The different regions of the mesoderm are then still
mutually dependent on each other (Yamada, 1937, 1939a, 1940,
1950). The origin of this dependence is still not clear (Muchmore,
1951) and it is possible [Chapter VI, section 1) that it is connected
with conditions which crowd or disperse the mesoderm cells.

Until they are invaginated, the anterior prechordal parts of the
mesoderm can develop into chorda or somites, but after it, they can
only form prechordal parts of the primary gut and mesenchyme
(Takaya, 1953a, b; Hoessels, 1957). They differ correspondingly in
their inducing effect on the ectoderm of the gastrula. Until invagination, prechordal mesoderm evokes the formation of posterior head
structures and in some cases anterior head structures as well. After
gastrulation, only anterior head structures are evoked, but even this
capacity weakens at the start of neurulation and is retained only in
the central prechordal plate (Takaya 1953a, b; Sala, 1955; Hoessels,
1957). At the neurula stage, the anterior head parts of the mesoderm become sharply differentiated from the posterior parts in
structure and inductive power, and still more differentiated from the
trunk parts. It is well known (Bijtel, 1931, 1936; Pasteels, 1939;
Chuang, 1947; and others) that urodele tail somites develop from the
posterior parts of the neural plate, and anuran somites at the end
of the tail develop in the same way (Smithberg, 1954). If ectoderm
of the middle gastrula is substituted for these parts, it develops into
tail mesoderm (Spofford, 1948), so apparently the mesoderm which
lies under them can only induce mesoderm. These experiments confirm that only neuralizing substances are transferred to the ectoderm
by the most anterior portions of mesoderm, and the nearer the tail,
the greater is the relative amount of mesodermalizing substances,
until in the last section, the neural plate develops into mesoderm
alone. The mechanism by which the substances are segregated within
the mesoderm is still not clear, but the process characteristically
leads to an increase in regional differences between its parts.

The influence of the mesoderm on the ectoderm changes not only
according to a change in its properties but to the duration of its
effect during gastrulation. If pieces of gastrula ectoderm are united
with pieces of anterior chorda from the neurula i.e. from the posterior
head region and are then separated at varying intervals, anterior
head parts develop after a short contact, and posterior head parts

develop after longer contact, or when the union is maintained (Johnen, 1956). In the same way, when hind-brain parts of the neural plate are separated from the underlying mesoderm and are united with pieces of ectoderm, the explants which contain only a little mesenchyme become rounded, like a forebrain, and sometimes even produce eyes (Takaya, 1955a). There is further evidence which also shows that inducing influences can spread for considerable distances in the ectoderm layer, and both these experiments and those quoted earlier on, show that the neuralizing substances spread further and more rapidly than do the mesodermalizing (Nieuwkoop, 1955b, Nieuwkoop and Nigtevecht, 1954). It therefore seems possible that the boundaries of the neural anlage depend not only on the local transfer of substances from layer to layer, but also on their subsequent distribution within the confines of the ectoderm itself.

Primary segregation in the neural plate in a lateral direction may be connected in the first instance not with the relationship between the different substances, but with the quantity and duration of the effect of the same factors. When the intensity is low and the effect weak, only derivatives of the neural folds, such as mesenchyme and chromatophores, are developed; a stronger effect causes various parts of the brain to develop, and these increase in scale in proportion to the strength of the inducing effect, up to the point where reasonably complete segments of brain are formed (Holtfreter, 1934a, b; Toivonen, 1940). This is the same series which develops when injuring media affect the gastrula ectoderm (see earlier). A similar series is obtained when the foreign inductors are placed under the ectoderm of progressively older gastrulae (Schmalhausen, 1947) and when the duration of their influence on the ectoderm of the gastrula is varied (Lopashov, 1939). Grafts of gastrula ectoderm made after preliminary ageing in saline (Holtfreter, 1938a; Gallera, 1952) up to neurulation, show the same series of formation and the shorter the period of explantation before grafting into the embryo, the more complete this is. Finally, when the mesoderm influences the ectoderm for different periods of time, the same series again arises, and the longer the period of contact, the more complete the structure will be; this effect was also found when different pieces of neural plate were explanted at different stages of gastrulation and neurulation (Gallera, 1948; Woellwarth, 1952) or when they were grafted into another embryo (Gallera, 1947; Damas, 1947; Dragomirova, 1949; Eyal-Giladi, 1954) or when pieces of ectoderm were united with anterior parts of the chorda at different periods (Johnen, 1956). Obviously the quantity of the acting substances or the length of time during which they can penetrate into the ectoderm, before the transition into the next stage of its development, are mutually involved with each other; in the areas where the quantity drops to a minimum which is unable to evoke the formation of a continuous layer of nerve cells, the neural fold derivatives are formed.

All this shows that during gastrulation the development of the cells of the embryo depends fundamentally upon the influence of substances acting in co-operation, on their concentration, and on the age changes of the cells themselves. The age-dependent properties of the cells of the ectoderm of the early gastrula are identical, and if this ectoderm develops in saline then age changes occur simultaneously in all of them; but some differences in the tempo of age changes appear in various parts of the ectoderm during gastrulation while the mesoderm is invaginating. The various mesodermal influences reach the different parts of the ectoderm at different times and this is very important in the rapid development of these stages; the process of differentiation ceases to be simultaneous in consequence; this is shown by the fact that in whole embryos the abdominal ectoderm loses its ability to develop into the different anlagen more quickly than when it is cultured in saline (Machemer, 1932; Gallera, 1953). It is also shown by the visible differentiation of axial structures which starts anteriorly and proceeds in sequence to the posterior end of the body. Pasteels' (1948, 1953a, b, 1954) experiments on centrifuged embryos (see earlier) show that an accumulation of cells in the early stages leads to the formation of mesoderm, and in later stages to the formation of neural tissues. In the same way, those parts of the embryonic disc of fish which invaginate late, react in a different way to the influences from the parts which are invaginated earlier. Similarly if the mesenchyme reaches the eye rudiment in early stages, it promotes the formation of pigment epithelium, but if the approach is delayed it does not. The scale on which similar phenomena take place in the development of the axial rudiment has still to be determined; where it has been possible to estimate their importance more precisely, this will be discussed later.

Nieuwkoop and his colleagues (Nieuwkoop, 1955a, b) have developed the idea that the origin of the parts of the neural plate depends on the following influences; firstly, an unspecific "activating" influence, which is analogous to the cytolysing effects by which

13*

Holtfreter evoked the formation of fore-brain structures; and secondly "transforming" influences which follow the activating one and cause the neural plate to form its posterior head and trunk sections. The latter influence does not act on the anterior section of the neural plate. The differences in the onset of these two effects are very slight, and it is most probable that they reflect the transfer of the two substances from the mesoderm, the neurogenic substances being more quickly transferred from layer to layer. They probably co-operate right up to the moment of transfer, and up to the start of neurulation, and already take part in determining regional peculiarities, including the size of segments of the neural plate. The inadequacy of the idea of regarding the primary influence as an unspecific one, which merely activates the inherent potencies of the ectoderm is clearly shown by Toivonen's experiments (1958). He showed that after brief treatment by mesodermalizing inductors, mesoderm but not neural tissue is the immediate result. Thus the usual terminology which emphasizes the contrast between the two kinds of influence cannot be regarded as satisfactory.

The same authors have attributed the regional organization of the neural plate, including the formation of its most posterior section and of the neural folds, to the influence of the "activating" and "transforming" factors. Thus the transforming principle has equally been held responsible for the dissociation of the cells of the neural folds to form the neural crest and the breaking up of pigment epithelium to form chromatophores. This last idea may seem to be supported by the fact that pigment epithelium develops best if in the vicinity of ectomesenchyme cells (Nieuwkoop, 1955a; Sala, 1956); but when the material is carefully examined there is no doubt that the reverse is true. Pigment epithelium develops best when it is plentifully surrounded by mesenchyme cells, including chromatophores, as this study has shown. It is therefore scarcely possible to accept the idea in its entirety, firstly because the two influences are not in opposition, and secondly because the transforming influence is composed of a great many different factors, which act both when the mesoderm exerts its primary effect, and in the later periods of development.

The idea of a succession of influences in the development of the neural anlage and the mesoderm is however an important one. Its value is simply that the mechanisms of development are changed by the periods of embryonic development which were discussed earlier. As in the case of the eye, the next development of the main rudiment is not a "self differentiation", but is accomplished with the participation of the new mechanisms which are formed on the basis of cellular properties arising in the previous stage. As the new period takes over the influence of the cells of one rudiment on another changes, and the reaction of the newly forming rudiments to these influences also changes. It is not always possible to make an exact separation between the mechanisms concerned in one period and those concerned in the next: experimental methods which combine and transpose parts in the gastrula and neurula have not elucidated the problem sufficiently.

The anterior part of the neural plate is evidently laid down as a result of more refined neuralizing influences. No matter how it is evoked, if the anterior head anlage is sufficiently large, eyes develop from it which separate from the brain. This is well demonstrated by Holtfreter's experiments on cytolysis. In normal development however the effect of the prechordal plate is not so restricted. When the parts of the anterior neural plate from which the eyes develop are exchanged with parts of presumptive hind brain, the optic zone develops into a part of the brain, and vice versa (Umanski, 1935). If these optic parts are rotated through an angle of 180°, the development of the forebrain does not alter (Alderman, 1935). At the same time the development of the optic part of the neural plate does change, according to how it is combined with different parts of the substrate. When a connexion is kept with the middle part of the substrate which normally underlies it, grafted optic parts always develop into eyes, and usually into pairs of eyes. When they are separated from it, the frequency of eye formation falls to 70–75 per cent, and usually only a single eye develops. In combination with the antero–lateral parts of the substrate the percentage of eyes formed falls still further, and when they are connected with the more posterior parts, eyes do not develop at all. In some cases, material from the immediate neighbourhood of the normal eye may develop into eyes, but this occurs more often when substrate is present than when it is not. When the substrate below the optic area is rotated 90° to the right, the right eye enlarges noticeably (Adelmann, 1929, 1930, Alderman, 1935), and when the median prechordal strip is removed, or lithium chloride is used to suppress its development, one cyclopian eye develops instead of two (Mangold, 1931, 1936; Adelmann, 1937; Lehmann, 1938). Obviously during the first or gastrulation period the influence of the substrate on the ectoderm effects the formation of the anterior head section of the brain—from which the eyes are later separated—but in the second, neurulation period, its influence is different. The prechordal plate continues to support the development of the fore-brain and the eyes which arise from it; but at the same time it acts to suppress the formation of eyes in the area lying immediately above it. The process of segregation within the neural plate depends on its connexions with the substrate. These become definitely localized and this leads to the development of a bilateral brain with paired eyes. Without these connexions with the substrate an anterior brain develops, from which a certain number of eyes will form, because of processes which occur in the neural anlage itself, but they then have a sort of spherical symmetry (Holtfreter, 1944c).

This applies also to the hind brain, since Holtfreter (1939) and Takaya (1955a, 1956) showed that the structure of its parts depends on its relations with the surrounding tissues, such as chorda, somites, and mesenchyme. Thickened masses develop in the brain wall where it comes in contact with somites; thin zones develop in the floor of the brain above the chorda, and these also form when it comes in contact with the glass in explants (Chapter II). Where the wall comes into contact with the mesoderm, vesicles develop with walls of varying thickness—some are completely thin walled. Takaya (1956) suggested that the different parts of the brain are still "undetermined" in the early neurula; the mesenchyme suppresses the ability of the neural plate cell to multiply and they therefore form thin walled vesicles. When isolated pieces of neural plate come into contact with the somites, cell multiplication is not suppressed, and the thick walled parts of the brain therefore develop.

At this point we also meet the phenomenon of the gradual segregation of the neural plate according to developmental periods. Comparison with the processes described in the present work (Lopashov, 1945a; Chapter II), shows that Takaya confuses processes which belong to two successive periods of development. The interaction of the neural plate and the substrate takes place in the neurula, when there is as yet no mesenchyme, though it takes effect later on. The regional differentiation of the brain along an antero-posterior axis is associated with the influence of the substrate, and in the neurula these regions—being still convertible into each other—keep their regional peculiarities when isolated; thus the eye is formed from the anterior region, and the induction of auditory vesicles by the posterior head region (Chapter II). When the most posterior neural plate is isolated and wrapped in ectoderm, it lengthens noticeably, and the explants develop in the form of little tails with unpaired fins (Aufsess, 1941).

The mesenchyme influence which counteracts cellular accumulations occurs in a later period of development; the experiments quoted earlier showed how this effect was produced both by a direct influence, and by helping the brain and eye to enlarge. The accumulations develop into retina in the eye and into thick walls in the brain. The chorda, which at first acts as do the other regions of the axial mesoderm, has a different effect on the later stages of brain development. By suppressing cellular concentrations, it helps bilateral symmetry to develop in the brain. In this way there is a gradual increase in specialization of the different parts of the brain. At first, its parts differ from each other in that in the absence of an opposing influence they will develop into the appropriate parts of the brain, although it is still possible for them to interchange their fates. Further subdivision of these parts occurs and is enhanced as the result of tissue interactions in the embryo, and as a result of the inter-relations of similar cells within any one tissue. Besides influencing the origin of the retina, such inter-relationships evidently take part in the separation of the brain walls, somites and blood anlage (Chapter IV, section 1). In somite formation the necessary condensation of mesoderm cells is further enhanced by contacts with the neural plate during its induction (Yamada, 1939b).

The nature of species differences in nearly all these processes is not clear. They are only understood for the period when the secondary influence of the mesoderm is essential to the development of the anterior section of the brain and the eyes. Different species may be arranged in a series, beginning with those which require this influence for the longest time, and ending with those in which the eye rudiments can develop autonomously in explanted or grafted pieces of presumptive neural plate. The series may be set out as follows, after data of Gallera (1947, 1948), Dragomirova (1949), Woellwarth (1952) and Johnen (1956):

1. *Triton taeniatus*
2. *Pleurodeles watlii*
3. *Amblystoma mexicanum*
4. *Bombina pachypus*
5. *Bufo viridis*

6. *Rana ridibunda*
7. *Rana esculenta*
8. *Rana temporaria*
9. *Rana arvalis*

The position of a species in this series is also correlated with the time at which the retina acquires a developmental stability within the area of the eye rudiment. These species differences are seen even more clearly in the rudiments of other organs which develop from the ectoderm in the third period of embryonic development, i.e. after neurulation is completed. The short analysis of the early mechanisms of their development which will be given later, is the last essential link in the comparison of the interaction of embryonic parts during development.

The origin of the *lens* is a classic problem of experimental embryology; the dependence of the lens on the influence of the eye which Spemann (1901, 1906) and Lewis (1904, 1907) discovered, provided the original example of the induction of one structure by another. Yet as soon shown, in many species of anurans, in axolotls and in other species of *Amblystoma* the lens can also develop when the eye is removed at the neurula stage (Spemann (1912, 1936, Mangold, 1931). The following studies gradually lead to the suggestion that other tissues from the head, i.e. the anterior wall of the archenteron, could also have an influence analogous to that of the eye rudiment (Mikami, 1939 b, Liedke, 1942, 1951, 1955, Hama, 1947). Direct evidence for this supposition has been obtained by Kawakami (1952), and by Jacobson (1955, 1958), who demonstrated the capacity of head endomesoderm to induce lenses from late gastrula and early neurula ectoderm in explants and whole embryos.

This and other data show that the succession of influences from head endomesoderm and the eye is not obligatory: either endomesoderm alone, or eyes alone can evoke the formation of a lens when grafted under the ectoderm of an embryo in its earlier stages (Waddington, 1936; Filatov, 1937, 1943; Lopashov, 1936, 1937; Woerdeman, 1938; Sheina, 1940, 1944). The experiments described in Chapter II, section 5 of this work show that when anterior parts of the neural plate, including the presumptive eyes, are combined with ectoderm from a neurula, the frequency of lens formation rises sharply with the degree of the contact. The action of the eye and the head endomesoderm are therefore probably similar, but the influence of the head endomesoderm apart from its basic effect, helps to form a closer contact between the eye rudiment and the ectoderm.

The influence of the head endomesoderm on the formation of a lens is not separate from its other influences. During gastrulation the origin of the anterior parts of the brain and the eyes is clearly associated with the influence of its dorsal parts, and the formation of the nasal placodes is also associated with its effect on the ectoderm (O. Schmalhausen, 1950). On the other hand, the nasal placodes can themselves evoke the formation of a lens when they are in contact with the head ectoderm in the eye region (Holtfreter, 1935a; Ikeda, 1938; Woerdeman, 1938). Nasal placodes can also develop in the ectoderm, under the influence of parts of the anterior brain (Haggis, 1956), or of brain appendages which have been isolated from the eye rudiment, or of the eye rudiment itself, after it has been kept in saline for 2 days (Chapters III and IV; Fig. 50). Lastly, Toivonen (1945, 1954), has shown that a lens can be evoked from the ectoderm by some foreign inductors of the anterior head type. When the culture period of isolated ectoderm is lengthened, its capacity to form lenses lasts longer than the capacity to form auditory vesicles and nasal placodes, and this in turn lasts longer than the capacity to form neural plate (Holtfreter, 1938a; Gallera, 1952). In all these examples, some common agents are probably acting, which produce different results according to differences in the age of the tissues concerned, and to their own intensity. When the influence is most intense in the gastrula stage, a neural plate is evoked, so that a lens cannot develop in this area; later on, it also becomes impossible for a lens to develop in the area of the nasal placodes. The lens forms in response to weaker influences which only reach the necessary threshold in later stages, or by stronger influences acting even later. The influence of the eye apparently complements the previous influence of the endomesoderm, the effect of the endomesoderm influence is increased sharply at the point of contact between the eye and the ectoderm, and this exactly localizes the place where the lens develops. The fact that the lens can develop more easily in the ectoderm lying over the eye, than in ectoderm removed from this position confirms this. Some substance obviously passes from the eye rudiment into the ectoderm and lens antigens develop in the ectoderm which were not formerly present in either one or the other, but which also develop when a mixture of their extracts is incubated (Woerdeman, 1953). The selective effect of the eye rudiment (Schmidt and Ragosina, 1937; Lopashov, 1937) has something to do with the fact that it makes contact with the ectoderm at a much later stage than the gastrula.

The species differences in lens formation occur because the relative roles of the head endomesoderm and the eye change from species to species, according to the tempo of changes in the ectoderm. In general, in those species in which a lens can develop even after the eye rudiment has been removed, it cannot develop from abdominal ectoderm of the same age under the influence of these rudiments. However, Filatov (1941 a, b, 1943) and Sheina (1940, 1944) showed that when eye rudiments were grafted earlier, into late gastrulae, lenses developed from the ectoderm in all the species which were studied. In *Rana temporaria*, which can form a lens from trunk ectoderm at the optic vesicle stage, lenses develop from late gastrula ectoderm in 100 per cent of cases; but in *Rana esculenta, Rana arvalis, Bombina pachypus* and axolotls, in which lenses cannot be induced in trunk ectoderm at the optic vesicle stage, lenses form in more than 50 per cent of cases from the ectoderm of the late gastrula.

Clearly the properties of the ectoderm change at different rates in different species. In the species where the trunk ectoderm loses its capacity to develop a lens early, the capacity to form a lens from lens-forming ectoderm also develops early. In species where the ectoderm changes at an earlier period, the appearance of the capacity to develop a lens is to a great extent associated with the precocious influence of the head endomesoderm. In other species the capacity is largely bound up with the eye rudiment. However, either the head endomesoderm alone or the eye alone, though particularly the latter, can cause the formation of a lens, when there is an alteration in other conditions, as for example in the age of the ectoderm or the strength of its contact with the eye.

Our information about species differences in lens formation is still incomplete; much of the evidence is contradictory—probably because the lens-forming material may not always have been completely removed from the eye rudiment (Stone and Sapir, 1940; Reyer, 1950, 1954, Lopashov and Stroeva, 1961). Generally speaking, the sequence in which the changes in properties take place is in the same order as the examples quoted earlier, with the important difference that axolotls and other *Amblystoma* species do not come between newts and anurans, but amongst the extreme varieties of anurans such as *Bombina, Rana esculenta* and *Rana arvalis*. Species differences of the actual eye rudiment evidently do not count for much in lens formation, since the inducing influence of the eye is endowed with some continuity. If the eye of tadpoles and adult

amphibians is unable to induce the lens from ectoderm, this induction
is possible at the stages from eye vesicle to the segregation of the
retina into layers (Reyer, 1954, Lopashov and Stroeva, 1961; and
Chapters III, section 4, IV section 4, and V section 7). Thus the mechanism which acts in the development of the lens is not characteristically
one which can be attributed to some local influence: it is one which
leads to a progressive increase and concentration of lens properties
in the parts of the ectoderm which lie opposite the eye, during which
the lens becomes involved in the general processes of eye formation
(Chapter IV, and Chapter V, section 5).

The origin of the *auditory vesicle* has much in common with the
origin of the lens. Both arise under the influence of the brain anlage
when it comes in contact with the ectoderm of the neurula (Stone,
1931; Harrison, 1935, 1938a, 1945: Kogan, 1940 and evidence
quoted in Chapter II, section 5 of this book). Both can also develop
as a result of influences from the mesoderm alone. If the neural
plate is removed from *Amblytoma punctatum*, *Bombina pachypus*
and *Bufo bufo* and the mesoderm is kept, the auditory vesicle
develops as it normally does (O. Schmalhausen, 1940; Harrison,
1935, 1938a, 1945) though it is slightly smaller in *Amblystoma*,
and is not subdivided (Yntema, 1955). Auditory vesicles develop
when pieces of chorda are grafted under the ectoderm of the neurulae
of newts and axolotls, but they are also small, and do not divide
into compartments (Kogan, 1944). When all the neural plate of an
early newt neurala is replaced by ventral ectoderm of the same age
new neural anlagen of variable size may be formed. In extreme
cases only a narrow tract or strand of neural cells arises above
the notochord; two auditory vesicles lie alongside this strand at the
level of the hindbrain. The thinner the strand the closer they lie
to each other. If no neural tract forms in the anterior part of the
embryo a single auditory vesicle arises above the chorda. It has
bilateral symmetry and is as large and well differentiated as normal
vesicles (Lopashov, 1941).

The localization of the auditory vesicle dorso-ventrally is closely
related to the age of the ectoderm from which it develops. It is obvious
that the chorda exerts its greatest influence in the mid-line, but
since the ectoderm is already in contact with the central parts of
the mesoderm at the gastrula stage, neural plate arises over these
parts, and auditory vesicles, displaced by the neural plate anlage,
arise along its edges. In the area where they normally develop,

the effect of the mesoderm—which is here too weak to evoke the formation of neural plate—completes and strengthens the effect of the neural plate as it rolls into a tube and comes into contact with the ectoderm. The competence of the ectoderm to develop into auditory vesicles is evidently achieved immediately following the period of competence to form the neural plate.

The antero-posterior disposition of the auditory vesicles cannot be attributed to restricted local influences. When ectoderm from a gastrula is grafted into a neurula or later stage, or grafts of gastrula ectoderm are made between anuran and urodele amphibians (Holtfreter, 1933a, 1935b, 1936), or when axial mesoderm is grafted under the periderm of a teleost fish (Oppenheimer, 1955) or foreign inductors are used, additional auditory vesicles develop both in front of and behind their normal site. An exact correlation is needed between the age of the ectoderm and that of the axial rudiment before their position can be precisely fixed. There is a definite balance between neuralizing and mesodermalizing substances in the mesoderm at the level of the auditory vesicles, and this probably also plays an important part in the formation of the ear vesicles. The fact that agents similar to those which are formed in the mesoderm emerge from the neural plate at this stage is proved by the fact that the neural anlage can induce more neural plate of the same level homogenetically (Mangold, 1933b; Spemann, 1936). If the relative ages of ectoderm and substrate are altered, the positioning of the auditory vesicles becomes less accurately fixed since a progressive limitation of the ear forming area to the normal site of the auditory rudiment cannot be achieved (Yntema, 1933, 1939, 1955). The mechanism of this progressive limitation is analogous to that which takes place in the lens, and is still obscure. Apart from anything else, it is probably connected with processes which are already taking place in the ectoderm of the auditory rudiment itself, following the effect of inductors.

The dependence of the formation of the auditory vesicle on the mesoderm and neural plate varies from species to species as in the case of the lens (Ginsburg, 1941, 1946 b, c, 1950a, b); when ectoderm from the prospective auditory vesicle area of ten species of amphibians was grafted at successive stages of development into the body and eye area, it was found that the frequency, size and structure of the vesicles increased regularly with time, though at different rates in different species (Fig. 66). This increase in specialization takes place

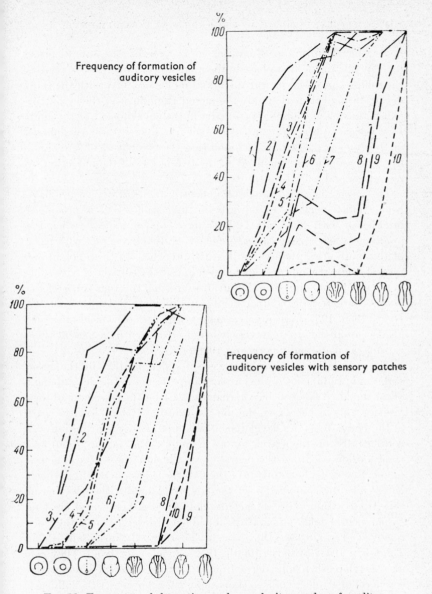

FIG. 66. Frequency of formation and complexity grades of auditory vesicle in amphibians after rudiment has been grafted at different stages into the abdomen of another embryo. 1. *Rana temporaria*, 2. *Bufo viridis*, 3. *Rana ridibunda*, 4. *Rana arvalis*, 5. *Rana esculenta*, 6. *Bombina bombina*, 7. *Pelobates fuscus*, 8. axolotl, 9. *Pleurodeles watlii*, 10. *Triturus taeniatus* (after Ginsburg, 1950b).

in two phases in urodeles, and in one in anurans, the anuran phase corresponds to the first phase in the urodeles. The first phase precedes the rolling up of the neural tube, and its first contact with the ectoderm; during this period only the mesoderm influences the ectoderm, and it thus plays a predominant part in the development of the auditory vesicle. When Yntema (1950, 1955) discovered these two phases in *Amblystoma punctatum*, he found that the two phases of sensitivity in the ectoderm corresponded to the two phases of the induction by mesoderm and neural tube.

The mechanisms of later development in the auditory vesicle have been studied very little; however an indication of their prolonged interaction with the brain in later development appears when the auditory vesicle anlage of *Amblystoma* is grafted in contact with parts of the brain other than those it usually touches. In these conditions typical compartments are not formed, and if the contact is with midbrain great swelling ensues. But after grafting to other zones of the body, characteristic compartments are formed (Detwiler and van Dyke, 1950, 1951). An intense swelling with loss of typical structure also occurs if the auditory vesicle is not enveloped by a mesenchyme capsule, as it normally is (Kaan, 1938).

The correlations in the processes of differentiation in the basic embryonic rudiments are even more important for the development of the unpaired *fin* of the larva, than they are for the lens and auditory vesicle; this is because the fin is continued over a large part of the body. When its development was first analysed, attention was concentrated on the search for its inductors (Hörstadius, 1950) and most authors regarded the neural crest, which is the source of neural mesenchyme, as the inductor of the fin. The neural mesenchyme itself enters into the composition of the fins by filling out the covering of skin from within. Fins in fact develop when either neural crest or earlier neural folds are grafted and do not develop when they are removed (Terni, 1934; Du Shane, 1935, 1938; Bytinski-Salz, 1936; Terentiev, 1941; Stroeva, 1950b, 1952; Bodenstein, 1952). They can also develop when mesoderm from a gastrula is grafted under the ectoderm of an older embryo (Lopashov, 1935a) or under the influence of the sub-caudal somites which arise from the posterior section of the neural plate (Aufsess, 1941), or after grafts of mesoderm from the somite region, or lateral plate of the neurula under the abdominal ectoderm (van Geertruyden, 1947). It seems therefore likely that the formation of the fins begins with the segregation of a strip of the ectoderm which lies along the edge of the neural folds, and can arise as part of a series: neural plate—neural folds—fin ectoderm, and under the influence of the neural crest.

This conclusion is also reached from the observation that the fin starts to form in a band of enlarged ectoderm cells, which is arranged above the neural tube and under the lower part of the tail bud. While the fin is growing and forming, in three main phases, this apical band always remains along its edge, but it disappears when the formation is completed. A fin cannot generally develop when this apical band is removed at the start of development, and if it is removed when the fin starts to develop, and before the mesenchyme has entered it, growth is stopped. A fin develops if the apical band is grafted into the side of an embryo (Stroeva, 1950a, b, 1952). Its role in the development of the fin thus seems to resemble the part played by the analogous thickening of the ectoderm at the apex of the limb and wing rudiments in birds (Saunders, 1948; Zwilling, 1949, 1955, 1956) and of the limb bud in amphibians (Tschumi, 1957).

Without going into the question of the nature of the interactions between ectoderm and mesenchyme during the development of the fins, it is important to notice how regional differences in the formation of the fins arise. The fin is absent from the head, and gradually increases in size towards the end of the body and the tail, where it reaches its maximum height. In the head, where there is no fin, the neural crest cells creep down much earlier than they do in the trunk. The ectoderm itself however differentiates in the various body regions with little differences in time, and because of this during the period of competence of the ectoderm, the neural crest in the anterior part of the body has already departed ventrally, while in the body region the age relations of ectoderm and neural crest correspond. When in fact the ages correspond, the head neural fold can evoke a fin in abdominal ectoderm (Stroeva, 1952). The processes of differentiation begin very early in the head, under the influence of the endomesoderm, and they lead to the formation of head organs such as nasal placodes, lens, etc. These processes are probably inimical to processes of fin formation. Actually, in experiments which supplemented those described in Chapter II, section 3, when the anterior quarter of the neural tube of a newt was explanted into the ectoderm of a late gastrula, rather shallow fins always developed above the brain.

Twitty and Bodenstein's (1941) experiments clearly demonstrate the age correlations between the ectoderm and internal rudiments of the embryo, and their species differences in urodeles. When lateral ectoderm is substituted for parts of fin ectoderm in *Triturus torosus* at the late tail bud stage (stage 26–28) fins develop in the anterior third of the body in 10·5 per cent of cases, and in the posterior third in 94·7 per cent of cases. When the grafts are made into younger stages (21–23), fins develop in the anterior third in 100 per cent of the experiments; this confirms that the capacity of the neural crest to take part in the formation of the fins falls off asynchronously from head to tail. Interspecific grafts of ectoderm from stage 26–28 of a series of urodeles into the anterior third of the body of *Triturus torosus* show that fin formation also depends upon the ectoderm. In one species, a fin was not developed in these experiments, in another it formed in some cases, as in *Triturus torosus* itself, and finally, it developed in every case in *Amblystoma californiense*. Thus, the area in which the fin develops is connected with the age correlations of the precursor anlagen, and differs from species to species according to the relative tempi of changes in the tissues of the anlagen. Species differences in the ectoderm are also shown up when the anlage of the apical band has been removed. In *Rana esculenta* and *Rana ridibunda*, *Bufo viridis*, *Bufo bufo* and *Pelobates* the band is renewed from the surrounding ectoderm; but in *Rana temporaria* and *Bombina* this does not occur, and no new fin develops (Stroeva, 1952). The narrowing down of the ectoderm region from which the apical band can develop obviously takes place at different speeds in the various species studied.

3. A General Outline of the Mechanisms of Embryonic Development

The regularities which have just been discussed are in many respects similar to those which were discovered during the analysis of the development of the eye. They do however provide more material for a determination of general regularities than the experiments on the eye were able to give. They, together with data from the development of the eye, make it possible to draw some more general conclusions about the mechanisms of development. As the information obtained from studying development of the lens, auditory vesicles and fins shows, the origin of these rudiments cannot be attributed to a local influence arising from a particular anlage. Such influences have some qualitative specificity, but, except in the case of the eye, they are not sharply localized. The physiological differences between the parts of the embryo are still not marked at these stages, and as the studies on inducing substances have shown, these differences shade gradually into one another. The mesoderm, the neural anlage which arise under its influence, and the neural derivatives, such as eye rudiment and neural crest, all still have a similar influence on ectoderm at any one level of the body of the embryo. The specificity of any developing anlage results both from such differences in the influences to which it is subjected, and from changes in time within itself, and also from tissue peculiarities which have already arisen. They should not be considered as purely quantitative time-space differences (Dalcq and Pasteels, 1947) or as purely qualitative differences.

The localization of organs in later stages depends not so much on the local influence of one rudiment on another, as upon more complex interaction of anlagen in which the correlations of time changes in different rudiments play an important role. The influence of the eye in localizing the lens must be seen not as a typical, but as an extreme example of localizing mechanisms. In the case of the fins, the changes in the ectoderm and neural crest do not take place simultaneously, and fins develop only at the sites where the time changes of interacting tissues come to accord. Auditory vesicles can be evoked by the influence of both the mesoderm and the neural anlage; but since the neural plate develops earlier under the influence of the median, more powerfully acting part of the mesoderm, the auditory vesicles, whose inception is associated with a further change in the properties of the ectoderm, are formed in the ectoderm immediately outside its limits. Similar time correlations in the course of changes in the different anlagen obviously begin with the actual invagination of the mesoderm during gastrulation. This not only increases the physiological differences between the parts along the axis of the body, but also leads to a difference in the rates of differentiation along its axis. There is also a lack of synchronization in the rate of development of different levels of the neural plate, but it is less marked here, and in the neural crest, than it is in the mesoderm. In the rest of the ectoderm it is even less noticeable. The localization of a number of rudiments is evidently connected with an exact coincidence of these changes, where the processes which lead to the development of a given rudiment begin to increase.

These age alterations of embryonic tissues changes vary from species to species. Since in one species a particular competence in the ectoderm may be reached earlier than in another, the influence of the mesoderm will play a dominant part in the origin of ectodermal rudiments in the first, and in the second both the mesoderm and the neural anlage may have an equal influence. Such a displacement or time shift may well be responsible for differences in the localization of a rudiment. In experiments each one of these influences can be the cause of a rudiment's appearance, when ectoderm of the appropriate age is selected. However, it is possible that in the normal development of some species, the primary influence prepares the ground for the next, as for example the influence of the mesenchyme prepares the urodele eye for the action of the blood. This is probably the explanation of the effect of the mesoderm on the development of the auditory vesicle in urodeles, and of the effect of the head endomesoderm on the development of the lens in axolotls, *Bombina* and other species, where the capacity to form a lens falls off more rapidly in the ectoderm.

Filatov (1939, 1941 a, b, 1943) revealed the significance of differences in the tempo of changes in the capacity of the ectoderm to form organ rudiments, and Ginsburg (1946 a, 1950 b) and Dettlaff (1956) developed his ideas further. The differences proceed from a shift in the tempo of development, which affects the whole of the ectoderm, and its capacity to form different organs. It has, however, already been shown that the rudiments do not form in exactly the same way in different species. Probably the tempi of changes in embryonic tissues vary even within large anlagen, and vary even more between different rudiments. In framing generalizations about these regularities, it is essential to use analyses from different anlagen and from different classes of vertebrates, instead of evidence drawn only from a small number of amphibian species.

During development, the peculiar properties of the anlagen increase and intensify, while the same processes which lead to their formation are suppressed in the surrounding areas. This may be seen in the relationships of the main parts of the eye, and also in the formation of auditory vesicles, lenses and the balancers (Balinsky, 1937) and in a series of other rudiments. The progressive localization of the capacity to form rudiments is not merely a consequence of the time at which a threshold of the required intensity of influence is reached, after which the next period of cellular changes automatically follows on. Simultaneously influences commence in the area around the rudiment which lead the ectoderm to develop in other directions, and prevent it from developing into the given rudiment. This also helps to localize

rudiments, and to increase their differentiation from their surroundings.

The phenomena of mutual reinforcement and inhibition which were
discovered in the interactions of the areas of the eye rudiment probably
also contribute to an increase in the distinctive properties of the various
rudiments. In the first part of this chapter a description was given of
the important part played in the development of several rudiments by
mechanisms involving mutual influence acting between homogeneous
cells, and producing a progressive increase in certain of their properties. Possibly such mechanisms may be discovered in other
anlagen by appropriate experiments. Although the whole story of
the complex mechanisms of mutual reinforcement can only be revealed
by special experimental studies, some information about the separate
links in the chain may be discovered by experiments on a number of
rudiments, as for example in the relationship between neural plate
and somites, or the apical ectodermal structures and mesenchyme in
fins and in the extremities.

The essential feature of developmental mechanisms, which has been
discovered in a variety of cases, is the fact that they are phasic. Period
specific changes in the mechanisms which form the rudiments are
found, not only in the eye, but in every other case which has been
sufficiently analysed, as for example in the formation of the fins and
the brain anlage. The mechanisms of a succeeding period can only
ensure that the formation of an organ is correct, if the way has been
been prepared for them by the correct accomplishment of the preceding period. The complicated structure of an organ cannot be built
all at once; new mechanisms must come into play during the later
periods, each of which complicates and develops further the structure
reached during the preceding stage.

One of the most important regularities ever established in experimental embryology, was discovered by Holtfreter (1938a) and
Gallera (1952), when they described the successive changes in the
ability of ectoderm cells developing in saline to differentiate into different rudiments. This is completely supported by the observation that
the ability of cells developing in a whole embryo to develop in a particular direction, according to circumstances, changes during the very
periods — with slight variations along the axis of the body — in which
the capacity of the main anlagen to turn into each other is lost. At
the transition from gastrulation to neurulation and during the closing
of the neural tube, these periods are common to many embryonic

14*

rudiments. Finally, this regularity also agrees with the fact that the rudiments of the neural plate and lens will not develop from the ectoderm earlier than the time at which they normally appear. The basic phases of this periodicity in eye development were described earlier (in Chapter V, section 7) and the first two periods are common to them and other major rudiments of the embryo. Besides the relative selectivity of the influences which lead to cellular changes, this sequence of changes is the most important mechanism in the process by which the rudiments are segregated in the embryo.

The phenomena which occur between the transition points at which the fate of the cells and rudiments acquire a definite stability are no less important than those which occur at the actual transition. In the ensuing period very significant gradual changes occur. Cells keep their capacity to convert within large rudiments such as neural plate and eye rudiment; but at the same time the differences between presumptive rudiments are increased. The cells also change morphologically: they may develop different structures, or change their shape or position and this may cause different invaginations, evaginations and rollings up. Such changes may to some extent anticipate the changes of the next period, and they can even finally themselves determine the course of events during the next stage. The mechanisms of progressive mutual strengthening and inhibition which have been described earlier (Chapter V, section 6), apparently occur during this phase of development.

These processes evidently lie at the root of whatever determines the fate of a cell, and establishes the stability of a cellular type over certain periods. The choice of path taken by cells during development is regarded by Holtfreter and Hamburger (1955) as a characteristic feature of induction, in which one rudiment has an influence on another. It is however already clear that while external agents can alter the basic cellular mechanisms of development, the development of the cells can also sometimes be directed by their own products. The concentration of these products can in turn be changed by the character of the relations of cells to the medium, and by the various interrelations between parts of the embryo; for example, by those which produce either concentration or dispersal of the cells, as in the influence of the ectoderm on the formation of the retina of the eye. Dependencies such as these are usually called inductions, and they can, at the stage when periodic changes in the fate of cells are going on, lead indirectly to changes in cell types. In other cases they

may have no such effect at all, but merely lead to the production
of interstitial substances, or to the formation of cell aggregations.
This last process evidently occurs in the formation of nephric tubules
under the influence of brain and mesenchyme, and in other dependencies which have been analysed by Grobstein (1955a, 1956). It is
therefore the character of their relation to the changes in cellular
properties and not the actual external dependence which is the most
important in determining the nature of the different mechanisms of
development.

The most important aspect of the study of the periodic changes in
cells is the problem of finding to what extent internal cellular processes
are associated with these changes, and on what structures the stability
of a cellular type is dependent. The genetical data have shown
very clearly how the hereditary pecularities of an organism depend
upon the nucleus (Wagner and Mitchell, 1955). This dependence is
especially clearly demonstrated by substituting the nucleus of one
species for the nucleus of another in the single celled alga *Acetabularia*
(Hämmerling, 1934, 1946, 1953), in the eggs of silk worms (Astaurov,
1937, Astaurov and Ostriakova-Varshaver, 1957) and of amphibians
(Dalton, 1946, Baltzer, 1947, and Sambuichi, 1957). But these experiments were all unable to decide how the nucleus and cytoplasm
participated in the mechanism of development, and in the appearance
of heterogeneous differentiations in cells of different types. It is still
uncertain whether the nuclei are solely responsible for the various
differentiations, whether their function actually changes during
development, and what leads to these changes.

Lopashov (1936) suggested that the nuclei do not remain unchanged during embryogenesis, and that their function alters with
the state reached by the cytoplasm during preceding development.
This suggestion is supported by Hämmerling's (1939) evidence that
the different states of the *Acetabularia* nucleus are dependent on
the influence of the cytoplasm. Further, the separate fragments of an
infusorian macronucleus are unequal in their capacity to support the
life of the protozoan cell, and this inequality depends on interactions
with progressive differentiations of organelles along the body of the
original organism (Weisz, 1951, 1954).

As far as the metazoa are concerned, it was long believed that their
nuclei were completely equivalent in all their cells. The prevalence of
this idea was based both on general genetic principles, and on Spemann's
classic experiments (1928, 1936); in these experiments, he constricted

an unsegmented newt egg in such a way that the nucleus remained in one half, which divided; at the sixteen blastomere stage he released the constricting loop, and one of the nuclei of the third generation crossed over into the unsegmented half. After subsequent separation— and when the loop was placed in a median plane—normal embryos developed from both these halves. Later on, Seidel (1932) demonstrated the equivalence of dragonfly nuclei by killing one of the first two nuclei. Those facts, however, only show that the nuclei are equal at these particular stages while experiments at the gastrula—neurula stage show that the differentiation in the embryonic cells only becomes stabilized at the end of gastrulation (Chapter VI, section 2). It seems likely then, that the nucleus does not alter before this stage; Spemann himself (1936, p. 135) agreed that only nuclear grafts could prove whether or not the nuclei remained identical throughout development.

When nuclei from the blastula–gastrula stage are grafted into whole unsegmented newt eggs or parts of them, the embryos with grafted nuclei only develop as far as the blastula stage (Lopashov, 1945c; Waddington and Pantelouris, 1953; H. Lehmann, 1955). In frogs however such experiments are more successful. When a nucleus from the blastula stage is grafted into an unsegmented egg, whose own nucleus has been removed, not only does the egg segment, but the embryo can develop into a normal tadpole (Briggs and King, 1952, 1953). Improved techniques were required to graft the nucleus from the smaller cells of later stages. It was then shown that endoderm nuclei taken from later gastrula or even tail bud stages are best able to support the differentiation of endoderm cells in the host embryo. The epidermis breaks down and falls away from the embryo. The neural plate is under-developed, and the structure of the somites is atypical. When mesoderm nuclei are grafted from a late gastrula, defects appear in the neural rudiment of the host embryo (King and Briggs, 1955; Briggs and King, 1957). These defects do not appear uniformly in all embryos. When endodermal nuclei are grafted from the same donor, a few embryos develop normally up to the tadpole stage, some have various developmental defects, and some do not develop beyond the blastula stage. When nuclei were taken from the ectoderm area of a blastula, which was itself the product of an egg previously given an endoderm nucleus, and the process of transfer was repeated serially up to four times, it was found that all the embryos bearing the descendants of the first original nucleus developed in exactly nuclei appeared in the embryos. This demonstrates both that nuclear changes are relatively stable and that the changes taking place in different nuclei of a single embryonic zone do not occur simultaneously (King and Briggs, 1956).

The data concerning changes in the nucleus during development correspond with what is known about the stages of cellular changes during development. A change in the function of the nucleus is a possible component of the basic cause of the origin of stability in the cell types of the various rudiments, which later subdivide into even more specialized cell types. The problem is then to discover the mechanisms which bring about these changes. All that is known about stages in cellular changes shows that the period of increase in cellular specialization is preceded by a crisis in cellular properties, and that this is obviously connected with one-sided changes in the composition of the cytoplasm. Since the cytoplasmic components evidently take part in either these or other links in the chain of cellular metabolism, it is possible that a predominance of certain cytoplasmic components guides it in their direction. The nucleus probably does not remain aloof from these general changes, because of all its possible functions, those which are involved in the chosen metabolic activities of the cytoplasm begin to predominate, until a stable phase is reached. After such a crisis or switch a new period of development commences, during which other functions within the possible repertoire of the nucleus are called upon.

A process such as this, involving the differential growth of specificity in cytoplasmic processes and nuclear changes may be repeated once, or several times in various anlagen, and even in a single anlage in different species of animals. The different tempi of changes in the ectoderm and other embryonic anlagen, which occur later on in those species of amphibia in which gastrulation and other fundamental morphogenetic processes begin after only fewer cell divisions (Dettlaff, 1956), may have something to do with the fact that in these species the increase in the specialization of the cytoplasm varies according to the ratio of the nucleus to the cytoplasm in each cell.

Beermann (1952, 1956), Breuer and Pavan (1955) and other authors discovered that in the giant nuclei of the Diptera the size of the different bands in the chromosomes increased sharply during development and for different tissues different combinations of such enlarged discs are characteristic. By using an electron microscope Beermann (1956) found that the separate "puffs" form loops which protrude from the ectoderm zone, defects which are characteristic of endoderm the same way; although the nuclei in the subsequent grafts were taken beyond the limits of the chromosome; this is similar to the condition in the "lampbrush" chromosomes of the germinal vesicle of amphibian oocytes (Koltzoff, 1938; Gall, 1958); the difference is that in the oocytes the whole length of the chromosomes is involved while in embryonic tissues, only distinct and strictly determined parts are concerned. It is likely that the changes which occur in nuclear function during development are connected with a similar selective activation of particular chromosome regions, which depends on the state of the cytoplasm, although so far it has not been possible to discover this in ordinary nuclei. There is, however, no need to suppose that in all animals similar mechanisms are responsible for the relationship between nucleus and cytoplasm during their development. Many nuclear functions may have mainly to do with oogenesis or the early stages of development; this is certainly true in many species of Diptera in which, from 20 to 80 chromosomes are eliminated at the beginning of development, except from the sex cells, leaving up to 4 chromosomes in the nuclei of adult animals (Beermann, 1956). In the same way chromosomes are also eliminated from somatic cells in other cases.

It is obvious that the function of the nucleus during development is not confined to the mere giving of "commands", which determine the course of development, since the nuclei themselves can change during development. It influences the differentiation of the cytoplasm according to the particular hereditary possibilities which are derived from the constitution and structure of its chromosomes. But it is likely, that from these possibilities, those which are appropriate to the cytoplasm after the processes of morphogenetic interaction have increased some and inhibited other of its properties, are selected and enhanced. The manner in which the nucleus takes part in individual development can hardly be perceived without the participation of such feedback relations, although the way in which nuclear factors act in the process of cellular differentiation is still not clear.

The connection of developmental mechanisms with nuclear functions can be one of the stable foundations of these mechanisms. On one hand the morphogenetic mechanisms operate during their stormy course on the genetic factors which are the material expression of evolution, and on the other hand they are tied to the environmental conditions. In spite of almost daily discoveries, the nature of their relations with the environment is less well understood today than is the connexion between development and nuclear function. This is certainly only because the connexion between the mechanisms of development and the environmental conditions has so many indirect components, each of which is conditioned by the various resources of the organism itself. They change continuously as the organs and tissues differentiate in the embryo. It is however through these steps, which lead to the alterations in the internal environment of the developing embryo that the conditions of the external environment are reflected in the timing and scale of the cytoplasmic differentiation, on which the introduction of the various nuclear functions and their quantitative expression depends.

The diverse morphogenetic mechanisms which arise and disappear so rapidly during embryogenesis are amongst these important foundations of development. No complete picture of causality in individual development can be built up without taking into account all the biological peculiarity of the relations between the three links in this chain. Morphogenetic connexions between parts cannot themselves be a sufficient cause of development but this does not mean that they do not enter into the causal mechanics of development, as a special link, characterized by the rapid course and direction of distribution of possible types of cellular differentiation within the confines of the organism. Different forms of dependence between parts, such as induction, mechanisms of cell accumulations etc. are not independent processes which by themselves lead to the development of the separate parts of the embryo. The real morphogenetic mechanisms are, on the contrary, characterized by the plurality of the links involved; the correlations between the separate components of the mechanisms which compose them are regularly transformed during the development of different species, according to the peculiarities of each species. This characteristic of the developmental mechanisms are obviously an expression of the fact that they have evolved as adaptations, designed to build up the complicated organism from the morphological simplicity of the egg in the shortest possible time. The separate links are naturally not important in themselves, but as the means whereby this possibility is achieved. All dependencies, which can progressively increase the special properties of the anlagen in the embryo are therefore found to be involved in its realization.

REFERENCES

ADELMANN, H. B. 1929. Experimental studies on the development of the eye II. The eye-forming potencies of the median portions of the urodelan neural plate (*Triton taeniatus* and *Amblystoma punctatum*). *J. exp. Zool.* **54**, 219–317.

— 1930. Experimental studies on the development of the eye III. The effect of substrate on the heterotopic development of median and lateral strips of the anterior end of the neural plate of *Amblystoma*. *J. exp. Zool.* **57**, 223–281.

— 1937. Experimental studies on the development of the eye IV. The effect of partial and complete excision of the prechordal substratum on the development of the eyes of *Amblystoma punctatum*. *J. exp. Zool.* **75**, 199–227.

ALDERMAN, A. L. 1935. The determination of the eye in the anuran. *Hyla regilla*. *J. exp. Zool.* **70**, 205–232.

ALEXANDER, L. E. 1937. An experimental study of the role of optic cup and overlying ectoderm in lens formation in the chick embryo. *J. exp. Zool.* **75**, 41–73.

ALGARD, F. T. 1953. Morphology and migratory behavior of embryonic pigment cells studied by phase microscopy. *J. exp. Zool.* **123**, 499–521.

ANDRES, G. 1953. Experiments on the fate of dissociated embryonic cells (chick) disseminated by the vascular route. *J. exp. Zool.* **122**, 507–539.

— 1955. Growth reactions of mesonephros and liver to intravascular injections of embryonic liver and kidney suspensions in the chick embryo. *J. exp. Zool.* **130**, 221–249.

ASTAUROV, B. L. 1937. Versuche über experimentelle Androgenese und Gynogenese beim Seidenspinner (Bombyx mori L.) *Biol. zh.* **6**, 3–50.

— 1948. The significance of experimental merogony and androgenesis for theories of development and inheritance. *Usp. sovrem biol.* **25**, 49–88.

ASTAUROV, B. L. and OSTRIAKOVA-VARSHAVER, V. P. 1957. Complete heterospermic androgenesis in silk worms as a means for experimental analysis of the nucleus-plasma problem. *J. Embryol. exp. Morph.* **5**, 449–462.

VON AUFSESS, A. 1941. Defekt- und Isolationsversuche an der Medullarplatte und ihrer Unterlagerung an *Triton alpestris* und *Amblystoma*-Keimen, mit besonderer Berücksichtigung der Rumpf- und Schwanzregion. *Arch. Entw. Mech.* **141**, 248–339.

BABURINA, E. A. 1948. The importance of light in the development of the carp retina. *Dokl. Akad. nauk SSSR* **61**, 399–402.

— 1949a. The development of the retina of the Amur bitterlings (*Acanthorhodeus*) in relation to the conditions of life. *Dokl. Akad. nauk SSSR* **64**, 869–872.

— 1949b. Adaptive peculiarities of integument of the embryo of the Amur bitterlings (*Acanthorhodeus*). *Dokl. Akad. nauk SSSR* **65**, 85–88.

— 1950. The development of the retina in *Hemiculer leuciscus*. *Dokl. Akad. nauk SSSR* **74**, 369–372.

BABURINA, E. A. 1955. The development of the eye and vision in herring *Alosa kessleri*. *Vopr. ikhtiol.* 4, 114–136.

1957. The development of the eye and its functions in the sturgeon and sevruga. *Tr. Inst. morf. zhiv. Akad. nauk SSSR* 20, 148–186.

BACON, R. L. 1945. Self-differentiation and induction in the heart of *Amblystoma*. *J. exp. Zool.* 98, 87–125.

BAER, K. E. VON. 1828 (1950) *Über Entwicklungsgeschichte der Tiere.* 1. Acad. Sci. SSSR Press, Moscow.

BALINSKY, B. I. 1937. Formation of balancers by defeat-experiments in newt embryos. *Dokl. Akad. nauk SSSR* 17, 495–496.

1939. Experiments of total extirpation of endoderm in newt embryos. *Dokl. Akad. nauk SSSR* 23, 196–198.

BALTZER, F. 1947. Weitere Beobachtungen an merogonischen Bastarden der schwarzen und weißen Axolotlrasse. *Rev. Suisse Zool.* 54, 260–269.

BARDEN, R. B. 1942. The origin and development of the chromatophores of the amphibian eye. *J. exp. Zool.* 90, 479–519.

BARTELMEZ, G. W. 1954. The formation of neural crest from the primary optic vesicle in man. *Carnegie Inst. Wash. Publ. 603, Contrib. to Embryol.* 35, 55–71.

BAUTZMANN, H., HOLTFRETER, J., SPEMANN, H. und MANGOLD, O., 1932. Versuche zur Analyse der Induktionsmittel in der Embryonalentwicklung *Naturwiss.* 20, 972–974.

BECKER, U., TIEDEMANN, H., und TIEDEMANN, H. 1959. Versuche zur Determination von embryonalen Amphibiengewebe durch Induktionsstoffe in Lösung. *Z. Naturforsch.* 14b, 608–609.

BEDNIAKOVA, T. A. 1947a. Formative action of the chorda on the development of parachordals in amphibia. *Dokl. Akad. nauk SSSR* 56, 977–979.

1947b. The character of the formative action of the chorda on the skeletogenic mesenchyme in amphibians. *Dokl. Akad. nauk SSSR* 57, 845–848.

BEERMANN, W. 1952. Chromosomenkonstanz und spezifische Modifikationen der Chromosomenstruktur in der Entwicklung und Organdifferenzierung von *Chironomus tentans*. *Chromosoma* 5, 138–198.

1956. Nuclear differentiation and functional morphology of chromosomes. *Symp. Quant. Biol.* 21, 217–232.

BERRILL, N. J. 1951. Regeneration and budding in tunicates. *Biol. Rev.* 26, 456–475.

BIJTEL, J. H. 1931. Über die Entwicklung des Schwanzes bei Amphibien. *Arch. Entw.-Mech.* 125, 448–485.

1936. Die Mesodermbildungspotenzen der hinteren Medullarplattenbezirke bei *Amblystoma mexicanum* in Bezug auf die Schwanzbildung. *Arch. Entw.-Mech.* 134, 262–282.

BIRSTEIN, J. A. 1941. Adaptation and evolution in cave animals. *Usp. sovrem. biol.*, 14, 436–453.

BODENSTEIN, D. 1952. Studies on the development of the dorsal fin in amphibians. *J. exp. Zool.* 120, 213–245.

BOTERENBROOD, E. C. 1958. Organization in aggregates of anterior neural plate cells of *Triturus alpestris*. *Proc. Nederl. Akad. Wetensch.* C 61, 470–481.

BRACHET, J. 1950. Quelques observations sur le mode de l'action de l'organisateur chez les Amphibiens. *Experientia* **6,** 56.

1952. The role of the nucleus and the cytoplasm in synthesis and morphogenesis. *Symp. Soc. exp. Biol.* **6,** 173–200.

BREUER, M. E. and PAVAN, C. 1955. Behavior of polytene chromosomes of *Rhynchosciara angelae* at different stages of larval development. *Chromosoma* **7,** 371–388.

BRIGGS, R. and KING, T. J. 1952. Transplantation of living nuclei from blastula cells into enucleated frogs' eggs. *Proc. Nat. Ac. Sci. USA* **38,** 455–463.

1953. Factors affecting the transplantability of nuclei of frog embryonic cells. *J. exp. Zool.* **122,** 485–505.

1957. Changes in the nuclei of differentiating endoderm cells as revealed by nuclear transplantation. *J. Morphol.* **100,** 269–311.

BYTINSKI-SALZ, H. 1936. Kombinative Einheitsleistungen in der Entwicklungsgeschichte. *C. R. XII Int. Zool. Congr. Lisbonne,* 595–618.

CAVANAUGH, M. W. 1955. Pulsation, migration and division in dissociated chick embryo heart cells *in vitro. J. exp. Zool.* **128,** 573–589.

CHANTURISHVILI, P. S. 1942. Evidence concerning the question of causality and of Wolffian regeneration. *Soobshch. Akad. nauk. Gruz. SSR* **3,** 261–268.

CHLOPIN, N. G. 1946. *General-biological and experimental bases of histology.* Ac. Sci. USSR Press, Moscow.

CHUANG HSIAO-HUI, 1939. Induktionsleistungen von frischen und gekochten Organteilen (Niere, Leber) nach ihrer Verpflanzung in Explantate und verschiedene Wirtsregionen von Tritonkeimen. *Arch. Entw.-Mech.* **139,** 556–638.

1940. Weitere Versuche über die Veränderung der Induktionsleistungen von gekochten Organteilen. *Arch. Entw.-Mech.* **140,** 25–38.

1947. Defekt- und Vitalfärbungsversuche zur Analyse der Entwicklung der kaudalen Rumpfabschnitte und des Schwanzes bei Urodelen. *Arch. Entw.-Mech.* **143,** 19–125.

CLAYTON, R. M. and FELDMAN, M. 1955. Detection of antigens in the embryo by labelled antisera. *Experientia* **11,** 29–31.

VAN CLEAVE, C. D. 1938. The effect of dead optic vesicle upon explants of prospective ectoderm. *Physiol. Zool.* **11,** 169–179.

COULOMBRE, A. J. 1956. The role of intraocular pressure in the development of the chick eye I. Control of eye size. *J. exp. Zool.* **133,** 211–226.

1957. The role of intraocular pressure in the development of the chick eye II. Control of corneal size. *Arch. Ophth.* **57,** 250–253.

DABAGHIAN, N. V. 1958. The role of the mesenchyme in the development of the pigment epithelium in Acipenser güldenstädti. *Dokl. Akad. nauk SSSR* **119,** 391–394.

1959. Regulative properties of the eye in the embryos of Acipenseridae. *Dokl. Akad. nauk SSSR* **125,** 938–940.

1960. Retina regeneration in the eyes of sturgeon embryos. *Zh. obshch. biol.,* **21,** 48–53.

DALCQ, A. and LALLIER, R. 1948. Le potentiel morphogénétique de la zone marginale dorsale chez la jeune gastrula du *Triton alpestris. Experientia* **4,** 309–310.

DALCQ, A. and PASTEELS, J. 1947. Une conception nouvelle des bases physiologiques de la morphogenèse. *Arch. Biol.* **48**, 669–710.

DALTON, H. C. 1946. The role of nucleus and cytoplasm in development of pigment patterns in *Triturus*. *J. exp. Zool.* **103**, 169–199.

DAMAS, H. 1947. Effet de la suspension précoce du flux inducteur sur la détermination du neurectoblaste médullaire. *Arch. Biol.* **58**, 15–57.

DEJEAN, C. 1939. Embryologie des diverses parties de l'appareil visuelle. *Traité d'Ophthalmologie* 1, 128–203. Masson, Paris.

DEJEAN, C., HERVOUËT, F. and LEPLAT, G. 1958. *L'embryologie de l'oeil et sa tératologie*, Masson, Paris.

DEL PIANTI, E. 1942. Ricerche sulla riconstituzione dell'abbozzo dell'occhio di Rana esculenta dissociato nei suoi elementi. *Arch. Zool. Ital.* **30**, 231–255.

DENIS, H. 1958. Influence de la méthode de l'élevage sur la différenciation nerveuse d'un fragment d'ectoblaste. *J. Embryol. exp. Morph.* **6**, 444–447.

VAN DETH, J. H. M. G. 1940. Induction et régénération du cristallin chez l'embryon de la poule. *Acta neerl. morphol.* **3**, 151–169.

DETTLAFF, T. A. 1938. Neurulation in anurans as a complex formative process. *Tr. Inst. exp. Morfog.* **6**, 187–200.

— 1940. Pecularities of the ectoderm of Anura. *Dokl. Akad. nauk SSSR* **28**, 669–672.

— 1941. Relative Bedeutung der Aussen- und Innenschicht der Neuralplatte bei der Bildung des Neuralrohrs schwanzloser Amphibien. *Dokl. Akad. nauk SSSR* **31**, 180–183.

— 1945. Differentiation of layers of the neural plate within the limits of the eye rudiment. *Dokl. Akad.. nauk SSSR* **50**, 509–511.

— 1946. Specification of topographical map of presumptive rudiments in anurans. *Dokl. Akad. nauk SSSR* **54**, 277–280.

— 1947a. Reversal of polarity in the ectoderm of Anura. *Dokl. Akad. nauk SSSR* **55**, 77–80.

— 1947b. Conditions for differentiation of ectoderm into neural tissue, epithelium and sucker. *Dokl. Akad. nauk SSSR* **58**, 501–504.

— 1956. The species differences and formative properties of germ material and the shift of gastrulation with respect to cleavage stages. *Dokl. Akad. nauk SSSR* **111**, 1149–1152.

DETWILER, S. R. 1943. *Vertebrate Photoreceptors*, Macmillan, N.Y.

DETWILER, S. R. and VAN DYKE, R. H. 1950. The role of the medulla in the differentiation of the optic vesicle. *J. exp. Zool.* **113**, 179–199.

— 1951. Recent experiments on the differentiation of the labyrinth in *Amblystoma*. *J. exp. Zool.* **118**, 389–401.

— 1954. Further experimental observations on retinal inductions. *J. exp. Zool.* **126**, 135–155.

DISLER, N. N. 1950. Problems of individual development in animals in light of the criticism of conceptions of development mechanics. *Usp. sovrem. biol.* **30**, 68–89.

DORRIS, F. 1938. Differentiation of the chick eye *in vitro*. *J. exp. Zool.* **78**, 385–415.

DRAGOMIROV, N. I. 1932. Über die Entwicklung des Augenbechers aus transplantierten Stückchen des embryonalen Tapetums. *Arch. Entw.-Mech.* **126**,
636–662.

1933. Über die Koordination des Teilprozesses in der embryonalen Morphogenese des Augenbechers. *Arch. Entw.-Mech.* **129**, 552–560.

1935a. Entwicklung des Augenkeimes nach der Implantation in der Gehirn-
höhle bei Pelobatesembryonen. *Tr. Inst. Zool. Biol. Akad. nauk Ukraine* **6**,
57–81.

1935b. Die Determination des Augenkeimes bei Amphibien. *Tr. Inst. Zool.
Biol. Akad. nauk Ukraine* **8**, 25–149.

1936. Über Induktion sekundärer Retina im transplantierten Augenbecher
bei *Triton* und *Pelobates. Arch. Entw.-Mech.* **134**, 716–737.

1937. The influence of the neighbouring ectoderm on the organization of
the eye rudiment. *Dokl. Akad. nauk* **15**, 61–64.

1939. Correlations in the development of ectodermal rudiments of the eye.
Izv. Akad. nauk SSSR ser. biol. No. **5**, 741–768.

1940. Duration of action necessary for the induction of the retina in amphibian embryos. *Dokl. Akad. nauk SSSR* **26**, 515–518.

DRAGOMIROVA, N. I. 1949. Species peculiarities in the age changes of ectoderm
in the eye region of amphibia. *Dokl. Akad. nauk SSSR* **66**, 533–535.

DU SHANE, G. P. 1935. An experimental study of the origin of pigment cells
in amphibia. *J. exp. Zool.* **72**, 1–31.

1938. Neural fold derivatives in the amphibia: pigment cells, spinal
ganglia and Rohon-Beard cells. *J. exp. Zool.* **78**, 485–503.

1943. The embryology of vertebrate pigment cells I. Amphibia. *Quart.
Rev. Biol.* **18**, 109–127.

EAKIN, R. M. 1947. Determination and regulation of polarity in the retina of
Hyla regilla. Univ. Calif. Publ. Zool. **51** (10), 245–288.

EBERT, J. D. 1953. An analysis of the synthesis and distribution of the contractile protein, myosin, in the development of the heart. *Proc. Nat. Ac. Sci.
USA* **39**, 333–344.

1954. The effects of the chorioallantoic transplants of adult chicken tissues
on homologous tissues of the host chick embryo. *Proc. Nat. Ac. Sci. USA*
40, 337–347.

ENGELHARDT, V. A. 1941. Enzymatic and mechanical properties of muscle
proteins. *Usp. sovrem. biol.* **14**, 177–190.

ENGLÄNDER, H. und JOHNEN, A. G. 1957. Experimentelle Beiträge zu einer
Analyse der spezifischen Induktionsleistung heterogener Induktoren. *J. Embryol. exp. Morph.* **5**, 1–31.

EYAL-GILADI, H. 1954. Dynamic aspects of neural induction in amphibia.
Arch. Biol. **65**, 179–259.

FERNALD, R. L. 1943. The origin and development of the blood island of *Hyla
regilla. Univ. Calif. Publ. Zool.* **51** (4), 129–148.

FILATOV, D. P. 1924. The fate of transplanted lens in newt larvae and the
reaction of the epithelium to the transplant. *Russk. Zool. Zh.* **4**, 1–13.

1925. Über die unabhängige Entstehung (Selbstdifferenzierung) der Linse
bei *Rana esculenta. Arch. mikr. Anat. u. Entw.-Mech.* **104**, 50–71.

FILATOV, D. P. 1927. Aktivierung des Mesenchyms durch eine Ohrblase und einen Fremdkörper bei Amphibien. *Arch. Entw.-Mech.* **110**, 1–32.

1932. Entwicklungsbeschleunigung in Abhängigkeit von einer künstlichen Vergrösserung der Anlage. Versuche an Amphibienaugen und -extremitäten. *Zool. Jb. Physiol.* **51**, 589–634.

1933. Über die Bildung des Anfangsstadiums bei der Extremitätenentwicklung. *Arch. Entw.-Mech.* **127**, 776–802.

1934. Determination processes in ontogenesis. *Usp. sovrem. biol.* **3**, 440–456.

1937. Über die Linsenbildung nach Entfernung des Chordamesoderms bei Rana temporaria. *Zool. Jb. Physiol.* **58**, 1–10.

1939. *Comparative-Morphological Trend in the Mechanics of Development, its Object, Aim and Course.* Acad. Sci. USSR Press, Moscow.

1941a. Über die historische Betrachtung der Erscheinungen der Entwicklungsmechanik und über ihre Bedeutung. *Zh. obshch. biol.* **2**, 3–18.

1941b. Some forms of connection between the mechanics of development and comparative descriptive morphology. *Tr. Inst. Citol., Gist. i Embr. Akad. nauk SSSR.* **1** (1), 59–66.

1943. Developmental mechanics as a method for study of some problems of evolution. *Zh. obshch. biol.* **4**, 28–64.

FINNEGAN, C. V. 1953. Studies of erythropoesis in salamander embryos. *J.exp. Zool.* **123**, 371–395.

FISCHER, I. 1937. Über das Verhalten des stoloniales Gewebes der Ascidie *Clavellina lepadiformis in vitro.* *Arch. Entw.-Mech.* **137**, 383–403.

FLICKINGER, R. A., HATTON, E. and ROUNDS, D. E. 1959. Protein transfer in chimaric Taricha–Rana explants. *Exp. Cell Res.* **17**, 30–34.

FOMIN, D. D. 1948. Induction of the sclera in foreign mesenchyme by means of action of the eye vesicle. *Dokl. Akad. nauk SSSR* **59**, 1361–1364.

FOSTER, M., COOK, R. and STAMAS, T. A. 1956. *In vitro* studies of the effects of melanocyte population density on melanin formation. *J. exp. Zool.* **132**, 1–23.

FÜRST, C. 1904. Zur Kenntnis der Histogenese und des Wachstums der Retina. *Acta Univ. Lund.* **40**, 1–40.

GALL, J. G. 1958. Chromosomal differentiation. *The Chemical Basis of Development,* 103–135. J. Hopkins Press, Baltimore.

GALLERA, J. 1947. Effets de la suspension précoce de l'induction normale sur la partie préchordale de la plaque neurale chez les amphibiens. *Arch. Biol.* **58**, 221–264.

1948. Recherches comparées sur le développement du neurectoblaste préchordale transplanté sur l'embryon ou enrobé dans l'ectoblaste *in vitro.* *Rev. Suisse Zool.* **55**, 295–303.

1952. Inductions céphaliques dans l'ectoblaste vieillisant. *Arch. Entw.-Mech.* **146**, 21–67.

1953. L'action d'urée sur les competences cérébrogènes et sensorielles de l'ectoblaste. *Rev. Suisse Zool.* **60**, 547–566.

GAYER, K. 1942. A study of coloboma and other abnormalities in transplants of eye primordia from normal and creeper chick embryos. *J. exp. Zool.* **89**, 103–145.

van Geertruyden, J. 1947. Formation d'appendices caudiformes aux dépens de greffons de mésoblaste postérieur chez les Amphibiens anoures. *Ann. Soc. roy. Zool. Belg.* **78**, 32–44.

Ginsburg, A. S. 1941. Transplantation of the ear ectoderm in axolotl. *Dokl. Akad. nauk SSSR* **30**, 546–549.

1946a. Changes in the properties of the ear ectoderm in the process of determination. *Dokl. Akad. nauk SSSR* **54**, 185–188.

1946b. Age pecularities of determination of the labyrinth in newt. *Dokl. Akad. nauk SSSR* **54**, 377–380.

1946c. Specific differences in the determination of the internal ear and other ectodermal organs in certain urodela. *Dokl. Akad. nauk SSSR* **45**, 557–560.

1950a. Age changes in the ectoderm of the ear region in frogs. *Dokl. Akad. nauk SSSR* **72**, 1195–1198.

1950b. Species pecularities of early stages of the development of the labyrinth in Amphibia. *Dokl. Akad. nauk SSSR* **73**, 229–232.

Giroud, A. 1957. Phénomènes d'induction et leurs perturbations chez les mammifères. *Acta anat.* **30**, 297–306.

Giroud, A., Delmas, A., Lefèbvres, J. and Prost, H. 1954. Étude de malformations oculaires chez le foetus de rat déficient en acide folique. *Arch. anat. micr. morph. exp.* **43**, 21–41.

Glees, P. 1955. *Neuroglia*, Blackwell, Oxford.

Grobstein, C. 1952. Effects of fragmentation of mouse embryonic shields on their differentiative behavior after culturing. *J. exp. Zool.* **120**, 437–456.

1955a. Tissue interaction in the morphogenesis of mouse embryonic rudiments in vitro. *Aspects of Synthesis and Order in Growth*, 233–256. Princeton Univ. Press.

1955b. Tissue disaggregation in relation to determination and stability of cell type. *Ann. N.Y. Ac. Sci.* **60**, 1095–1106.

1956. Trans-filter induction of tubules in mouse metanephrogenic mesenchyme. *Exp. Cell Res.* **10**, 424–440.

Grobstein, C. and Zwilling, E. 1953. Modification of growth and differentiation of chorioallantoic grafts of chick blastoderm pieces after cultivation at a glass-clot interface. *J. exp. Zool.* **122**, 259–284.

Güttes, E. 1953a. Die Herkunft des Augenpigments beim Kaninchenembryo. *Z. Zellf.* **39**, 168–202.

1953b. Über die Beeinflussung der Pigmentgenese im Auge des Hühnerembryos durch Röntgenstrahlen und über die Herkunft der Pigmentgranula. *Z. Zellf.* **39**, 260–275.

Haggis, A. J. 1956. Analysis of the determination of the olfactory placode in *Amblystoma punctatum*. *J. Embryol. exp. Morph.* **4**, 120–138.

Hama, T. 1947. Formation of free lenses with special reference to the role of the endoderm. *Zool. Mag. (Japan)* **57**, 65–66.

Hämmerling, J. 1934. Entwicklungsphysiologische und genetische Grundlagen der Formbildung bei der Schirmalge *Acetabularia*. *Naturwiss.* **22**, 829–836.

1939. Über die Bedingungen der Kernteilung und der Zystenbildung bei *Acetabularia mediterranea*. *Biol. Zbl.* **59**, 158–193.

HÄMMERLING, J. 1946. Neue Untersuchungen über die physiologischen und genetischen Grundlagen der Formbildung. (Nach Versuchen an der Schirmalge *Acetabularia* und ihren Verwandten.) *Naturwiss.* **33**, 337–342 and 361–365.

1953. Nucleo-cytoplasmic relationships in the development of *Acetabularia. Int. Rev. Cytol.* **2**, 475–498.

HARRISON, R. G. 1910. The outgrowth of the nerve fiber as a mode of protoplasmic movement. *J. exp. Zool.* **9**, 787–848.

1933. Some difficulties of the determination problem. *Am. Nat.* **67**, 306–321.

1935. Factors concerned in the development of the ear in *Amblystoma punctatum. Anat. Rec.* **64**, suppl. 1, 38–39.

1938a. Further investigations of the factors concerned in the development of the ear. *Anat. Rec.* **70**, suppl. 3, 35.

1938b. Die Neuralleiste. *Verh. anat. Ges.* **85**, Erg.-H. 4–30.

1945. Relations of symmetry in the developing embryo. *Trans. Conn. Ac. Art. Sci.* **36**, 277–330.

HARROW, B. and MAZUR, A. 1955. *Textbook of Biochemistry.* Saunders, Philadelphia and London.

HASEGAWA, M. 1958. Restitution of the eye after removal of the retina and lens in the newt, *Triturus pyrrhogaster. Embryologia* **4**, 1–32.

HAYASHI, Y. 1955. Inductive effect of some fractions of tissue extracts after removal of pentose nucleic acid, tested on the isolated ectoderm of *Triturus* gastrula. *Embryologia* **2**, 145–162.

1956. Morphogenetic effects of pentose nucleoprotein from the liver upon the isolated ectoderm. *Embryologia* **3**, 57–67.

1958. The effects of pepsin and trypsin on the inductive ability of pentose nucleoprotein from guinea pig liver. *Embryologia* **4**, 33–53.

HOESSELS, E. L. M. 1957. *Évolution de la plaque préchordal d'Amblystoma mexicanum; sa differentiation propre et sa puissance industrice pendant la gastrulation.* Diss., Druck J. Stegen, Maastricht.

HOLTFRETER, J. 1931. Über die Aufzucht isolierter Teile des Amphibienkeimes II. Züchtung von Keimen und Keimteilen in Salzlösung. *Arch. Entw.-Mech.* **124**, 404–466.

1933a. Der Einfluß von Wirtsalter und verschiedenen Organbezirken auf die Differenzierung von angelagertem Gastrulaektoderm. *Arch. Entw.-Mech.* **127**, 619–775.

1933b. Nachweis der Induktionsfähigkeit abgetöteter Keimteile. *Arch. Entw.-Mech.* **128**, 584–633.

1933c. Organisierungsstufe nach regionaler Kombination von Entomesoderm mit Ektoderm. *Biol. Zbl.* **53**, 404–431.

1934a. Der Einfluß thermischer, mechanischer und chemischer Eingriffe auf die Induzierfähigkeit von Triton-Keimteilen. *Arch. Entw.-Mech.* **132**, 255–306.

1934b. Über die Verbreitung induzierender Substanzen und ihre Leistungen im Triton-Keim. *Arch. Entw.-Mech.* **132**, 307–383.

1934c. Formative Reize in der Embryonalentwicklung der Amphibien, dargestellt an Explantationsversuchen. *Arch. exp. Zellf.* **15**, 281–301.

HOLTFRETER, J. 1935a. Morphologische Beeinflussung von Urodelenektoderm bei xenoplastischer Transplantation. *Arch. Entw.-Mech.* **133**, 367–426.

1935b. Über das Verhalten von Anurenektoderm in Urodelenkeimen. *Arch. Entw.-Mech.* **133**, 427–494.

1936. Regionale Induktionen in xenoplastisch zusammengesetzten Explantaten. *Arch. Entw.-Mech.* **134**, 466–550.

1938a. Veränderungen der Reaktionsweise in alternden isolierten Gastrulaektoderm. *Arch. Entw.-Mech.* **138**, 163–196.

1938b. Differenzierungspotenzen isolierter Teile der Urodelengastrula. *Arch. Entw.-Mech.* **138**, 522–656.

1938c. Differenzierungspotenzen isolierter Teile der Anurengastrula. *Arch. Entw.-Mech.* **138**, 657–738.

1939. Gewebeaffinität, ein Mittel der embryonalen Formbildung. *Arch. exp. Zellf.* **23**, 169–209.

1943a. Properties and functions of the surface coat in amphibian embryos. *J. exp. Zool.* **93**, 251–323.

1943b. A study of the mechanics of gastrulation I. *J. exp. Zool.* **94**, 261–318.

1944a. A study of the mechanics of gastrulation II. *J. exp. Zool.* **95**, 171–212.

1944b. Experimental studies on the development of the pronephros. *Rev. Canad. biol.* **3**, 220–250.

1944c. Neural differentiation of ectoderm through exposure to saline solution. *J. exp. Zool.* **95**, 307–343.

1945. Neuralisation and epidermization of gastrula ectoderm. *J. exp. Zool.* **98**, 161–209.

1946. Structure, motility and locomotion in isolated embryonic amphibian cells. *J. Morphol.* **79**, 27–62.

1947. Changes of structure and the kinetics of differentiating embryonic cells. *J. Morphol.* **80**, 57–92.

1948a. Concepts on the mechanism of embryonic induction and its relation to parthenogenesis and malignancy. *Symp. Soc. exp. Biol.* **2**, 17–49.

1948b. Significance of cell membrane in embryonic processes. *Ann.N.-Y. Ac. Sci.* **49**, 709–760.

1951. Some aspects of embryonic induction. 10 *Growth Symp.* 117–152.

HOLTFRETER, J. and HAMBURGER, V. 1955. Embryogenesis: Progressive Differentiation. Amphibians. *Analysis of Development.* 230–296. Saunders, Philadelphia and London.

HÖRSTADIUS, S. 1950. *The Neural Crest.* Oxford University Press.

HÖRSTADIUS, S. und SELLMAN, S. 1946. Experimentelle Untersuchungen über die Determination des knorpeligen Kopfskelettes bei Urodelen. *Nova Acta Reg. Soc. Scient. Upsal.* ser. IV, **13**, 1–170.

HUMM, D. G. 1953. The measurement of nitrogen constituents in the blood of developing salamander larvae. *J. exp. Zool.* **124**, 241–262.

ICHIKAWA, M. 1937. Experiments on the amphibian mesectoderm, with special reference to the cartilage-formation. *Mem. Coll. Sci. Kyoto Imp. Univ. B* **12**, 311–351.

IKEDA, Y. 1935. Über die Regeneration von Augenbechern an verschiedenen Körperstellen durch isolierte Irisstücke. *Arb. anat. Inst. japan. Univ. Sendai* **17**, 11–54.

— 1938. Über die wechselseitigen Beziehungen der Sinnesorgane untereinander in ihrer normalen und experimentell bedingten Entwicklung. *Arb. anat. Inst. japan. Univ. Sendai* **21**, 1–44.

JACOBSON, A. G. 1955. The role of the optic vesicle and other head tissues in lens induction. *Proc. Nat. Ac. Sci. USA* **41**, 522–525.

— 1958. The roles of neural and non-neural tissues in lens induction. *J. exp. Zool.* **139**, 527–557.

JOHNEN, A. G. 1956. Experimental studies about the temporal relationship in the induction process I, II. *Proc. Nederl. Akad. Wetench.* C **59**, 554–561 and 652–660.

JOLLY, J. 1944. Recherches sur la formation du systeme vasculaire des Batraciens. *Bull. biol. Fr. Belg.* **78**, 124–135.

KAAN, H. W. 1938. Further studies of the auditory vesicle and cartilaginous capsule of *Amblystoma punctatum*. *J. exp. Zool.* **78**, 159–180.

KARASAKI, S. and YAMADA, T. 1955. Morphogenetic effects of centrifugation on the isolated ectoderm and whole embryo of some Anurans. *Experientia* **11**, 191–194.

KAWAKAMI, I. 1952. Relation of inductive effect to embryonic field, with special reference to the developmental mechanism of cephalic sensory organs in amphibians. *Annot. zool. japan.* **25**, 97–104.

KEMP, N. E. 1953. Morphogenesis and metabolism of amphibian larvae after excision of the heart I. Morphogenesis of heartless tadpoles of *Rana pipiens*. *Anat. Rec.* **117**, 405–425.

KEMP, N. E. and QUINN, B. L. 1954. Morphogenesis and metabolism of amphibian larvae after excision of the heart II. Morphogenesis of heartless larvae of *Amblystoma punctatum*. *Anat. Rec.* **118**, 773–787.

KING, T. J. and BRIGGS, R. 1955. Changes in the nuclei of differentiating gastrula cells, as demonstrated by nuclear transplantation. *Proc. Nat. Ac. Sci. USA* **41**, 321–325.

— 1956. Serial transplantation of embryonic nuclei. *Symp. Quant. Biol.* **21**, 271–290.

KNOWER, H. M. E. 1907. Effects of early removal of the heart and arrest of circulation on the development of frog embryos. *Anat. Rec.* **1**, 161–165.

KOGAN, R. E. 1940. The induction effect of the oblongata upon the body epithelium of amphibians. *Tr. Inst. exp. Morfog.* **7**, 47–54.

— 1944. Chordamesoderm as an inductor of ear vesicles. *Dokl. Akad. nauk SSSR* **45**, 42–45.

KOLOSS, E. I. 1949. Some data concerning the contractile components of the iris of the frog eye. *Dokl. Akad. nauk SSSR* **66**, 1175–1178.

KOLTZOFF, N. K. 1938. The structure of chromosomes and their participation in cell metabolism. *Biol. Zh.* **7**, 3–46.

KORZHUEV, P. A. 1952. On the types of localization and the quantity of haemoglobin in the blood of various animals. *Usp. sovrem. biol.* **33**, 391–408.

15*

KRYZHANOVSKY, S. G. 1949. Ecologic-morphological regularities in the development of cyprinid, cobitid and silurid fishes. *Tr. Inst. morf. zhiv. Akad. nauk SSSR* 1, 5—332.

—— 1950. Theoretical foundations of embryology. *Usp. sovrem. biol.* **30**, 382—413.

KRYZHANOVSKY, S. G., DISLER, N. N. and SMIRNOVA, E. N. 1953. Ecologic-morphological regularities in the development of perciform fishes. *Tr. Inst. morf. zhiv. Akad. nauk. SSSR* **10**, 3—138.

KUUSI, T. 1951. Über die chemische Natur der Induktionsstoffe. *Ann. Zool. Soc. Fenn. Vanamo* **14**, 1—98.

—— 1957. On the properties of the mesoderm inductor I. *Arch. Soc. zool. bot. Fenn. Vanamo* **11**, 136—148.

LANGMAN, J. 1953. Tissue culture and serological experiments. *Proc. Nederl. Akad. Wetensch.* C **56**, 219—227.

LEHMANN, F. E. 1933. Das Prinzip der kombinativen Einheitsleistung in der Biologie. *Biol. Zbl.* **53**, 471—496.

—— 1934. Die Linsenbildung von *Rana fusca* in ihrer Abhängigkeit von chemischen Einflüssen. *Arch. Entw.-Mech.* **131**, 333—361.

—— 1936. Die chemische Beeinflußbarkeit der Linsenbildung bei verschiedenen Temperaturen. *Arch. Entw.-Mech.* **134**, 166—199.

—— 1937. Mesodermisierung des präsumptiven Chordamaterials durch Einwirkung von Lithiumchlorid auf die Gastrula von Triton alpestris. *Arch. Entw.-Mech.* **136**, 112—146.

—— 1938. Regionale Verschiedenheiten des Organisators von Triton, nachgewiesen durch phasenspezifische Erzeugung von lithiumbedingten und operativ bewirkten Regionaldefekten. *Arch. Entw.-Mech.* **138**, 106—158.

—— 1945. *Einführung in die physiologische Embryologie.* Birkhäuser, Basel.

—— 1950. Die Morphogenese in ihrer Abhängigkeit von elementaren biologischen Konstituenten des Plasmas. *Rev. Suisse Zool.* **57**, suppl. 1, 141—151.

LEHMAN, H. E. 1955. On the development of enucleated *Triton* eggs with an injected blastula nucleus. *Biol. Bull.* **108**, 138—150.

LEVANDER, G. 1945. Tissue induction. *Nature* **155**, 148—149.

LEWIS, W. H. 1904. Experimental studies on the development of the eye in Amphibia I. On the origin of the lens in *Rana palustris*. *Am. J. Anat.* **3**, 505—536.

—— 1907. Experiments on the origin and differentiation of the optic vesicle in amphibia. *Am. J. Anat.* **7**, 259—277.

LIEDKE, K. B. 1942. Lens competence in *Rana pipiens*. *J. exp. Zool.* **90**, 331—351.

—— 1951. Lens competence in *Amblystoma punctatum*. *J. exp. Zool.* **117**, 573—591.

—— 1955. Studies on lens induction in *Amblystoma punctatum*. *J. exp. Zool.* **130**, 353—379.

LOPASHOV, G. V. 1935a. Über die Ausbildung von regionalen Verschiedenheiten im Mesoderm der Amphibiengastrula. *Biol. Zh.* **4**, 429—446.

—— 1935b. Die Entwicklungsleistungen des Gastrulamesoderms in Abhängigkeit von Veränderungen seiner Masse. *Biol. Zbl.* **55**, 606—615.

Lopashov, G. V. 1936. Eye inducing substances. *Biol. Zh.* **5**, 463–488.

   1937. Über die Spezifiität induktiver Einflüsse. *Dokl. Akad. nauk SSSR* **15**, 286–288.

   1939. On the character of cell changes in neural plate induction. *Dokl. Akad. nauk SSSR* **24**, 205–208.

   1941. Formbildungsfelder des Mesoderms bei Amphibienkiemen. *Akad. nauk SSSR*, **30**, 770–774.

   1944. Origin of pigment cells and visceral cartilage in teleosts. *Dokl. Akad. nauk SSSR* **44**, 169–172.

   1945a. On some simplest processes of organization of eye and brain rudiments in urodelan embryos. *Dokl. Akad. nauk SSSR* **48**, 605–608.

   1945b. Sources of origin of tissues in vertebrate embryogenesis. *Usp. sovrem. biol.* **20**, 155–186.

   1945c. Experimental study on potencies of nuclei from newt blastulae by means of transplantation. *Ref. rab. biol. Otd. Akad. nauk SSSR*, 88–89.

   1946. Ground processes of eye organization in amphibians. *Dokl. Akad. nauk SSSR* **53**, 177–180.

   1948a. Significance of mesenchyme envelopes in the development of the eyes in amphibians. *Dokl. Akad. nauk SSSR* **60**, 1281–1284.

   1948b. On the significance of the lens and the inner limiting sheet in the formation of the eyes in amphibia. *Dokl. Akad. nauk SSSR* **61**, 581–584.

   1949. On the significance of different processes in the restoration of amphibian eyes. *Dokl. Akad. nauk SSSR* **69**, 865–868.

   1951. Metabolic conditions of the eye rudiments and the paths of their development. *Dokl. Akad. nauk SSSR* **77**, 933–936.

   1955. On the quantitative regularities in regeneration of the retina. *Dokl. Akad. nauk SSSR* **105**, 599–602.

   1956. Mechanisms of formation and origin of choroid coat in the amphibian eye. *Dokl. Akad. nauk SSSR* **109**, 653–656.

   1959. Comparative studies of the transformation capacity of the eye layers at various stages of development in vertebrates. *Proc. XV Int. Zool. Congr. London*, 613–615.

Lopashov, G. V. and Stroeva, O. G. 1961. Morphogenesis of the vertebrate eye. *Adv. Morphog.* **1**, 331–377.

Lucas, D. R. and Trowell, O. A. 1958. *In vitro* culture of the eye and the retina of the mouse and rat. *J. Embryol. exp. Morph.* **6**, 178–182.

Luther, W. 1935. Entwicklungsphysiologische Untersuchungen am Forellenkeim: Die Rolle des Organisationszentrums bei der Entstehung der Embryonalanlage. *Biol. Zbl.* **55**, 114–137.

   1936. Potenzprüfungen an isolierten Teilstücken der Forellenkeimscheibe. *Arch. Entw.-Mech.* **135**, 359–383.

   1937. Transplantations- und Defektversuche am Organisationszentrum der Forellenkeimscheibe. *Arch. Entw.-Mech.* **137**, 404–424.

Machemer, H. 1932. Experimentelle Untersuchungen über die Induktionsleistungen der oberen Urmundlippe im älteren Urodelenkeimen. *Arch. Entw.-Mech.* **126**, 391–456.

Malinovsky, A. A. 1945. Types of interaction and their significance in the organism. *Ref. rab. biol. Otd. Akad. nauk SSSR*, 292–293.

MANGOLD, O. 1931. Das Determinationsproblem III. Das Wirbeltierauge in der Entwicklung und Regeneration. *Erg. Biol.* **7**, 193–403.

1933a. Isolationsversuche zur Analyse der Entwicklung bestimmter Kopforgane *Naturwiss.* **21**, 394–397.

1933b. Über die Induktionsfähigkeit der verschiedenen Bezirke der Neurula von Urodelen. *Naturwiss.* **21**, 761–766.

1936. Experimente zur Analyse der Zusammenarbeit der Keimblätter. *Naturwiss.* **24**, 753–760.

MANN, I. 1957. *Developmental Abnormalities of the Eye.* Brit. Med. Assoc., London.

MCKEEHAN, M. S. 1954. A quantitative study of self-differentiation of transplanted lens primordia in the chick. *J. exp. Zool.* **126**, 157–175.

MIKAMI, Y. 1939a. Reciprocal transformations of the parts in the developing eye-vesicle, with special reference to the inductive influence of lens-ectoderm on the retinal differentiation. *Zool. Mag. (Japan)* **51**, 253–256.

1939b. Lens-induction in the urodelan Triturus, with special reference to the free formation of the lens. *Mem. Coll. Sci. Kyoto Imp. Univ.* B **15**, 134–157.

MOSCONA, A. 1957. Formation of lentoids by dissociated retinal cells of the chick embryo. *Science* **125**, 598–599.

MOSER, F. 1940. The differentiation of isolated gills of the amphibian embryo. *J. Morphol.* **66**, 261–275.

MUCHMORE, W. B. 1951. Differentiation of the trunk mesoderm in *Amblystoma maculatum. J. exp. Zool.* **118**, 137–186.

1957. Differentiation of the trunk mesoderm in *Amblystoma maculatum* II. Relation of the size of presumptive somite explants to subsequent differentiation. *J. exp. Zool.* **134**, 293–313.

NACE, G. W. 1953. Serological studies of the blood of the developing chick embryo. *J. exp. Zool.* **122**, 423–448.

NEYFAKH, A. A. 1951. The development of the chick eye on the chorioallantois. *Dokl. Akad. nauk SSSR* **81**, 949–952.

NIEUWKOOP, P. D. (a. coll.) 1955a. Origin and establishment of organization patterns in embryonic fields during early development in amphibans and birds, in particular in the nervous system and its substrate. *Proc. Nederl. Akad. Wetensch.* C 58, 219–227 and 356–367.

1955b. Independent and dependent development in the formation of the central nervous system in amphibians. *Exp. Cell Res.* suppl. 3, 262–273.

NIEUWKOOP, P. D. and FABER, J. 1956. *Normal table of Xenopus laevis.* North-Holland Publ. Co., Amsterdam.

NIEUWKOOP, P. D. and NIGTEVECHT, G. N. 1954. Neural activation and transformation in explants of competent ectoderm under the influence of fragments of anterior notochord in urodeles. *J. Embryol. exp. Morph.* **2**, 175–193.

NIU, M.-C. 1947. The axial organization of neural crest, studied with particular reference to its pigmentary component. *J. exp. Zool.* **195**, 79–113.

1954. Further studies of the origin of amphibian pigment cells. *J. exp. Zool.* **125**, 199–220.

Niu, M.-C. 1956. New approaches to the problem of embryonic induction. *Cellular Mechanisms in Differentiation and Growth*, 155–171. Princeton Univ. Press.

— 1958a. The role of ribonucleic acid in embryonic differentiation. *Anat. Rec.* **131**, 585.

— 1958b. Thymus ribonucleic acid and embryonic differentiation *Proc. Nat. Ac. Sci. USA* **44**, 1264–1274.

Niu, M.-C. and Twitty, V. C. 1953. The differentiation of gastrula ectoderm in medium conditioned by axial mesoderm. *Proc. Nat. Ac. Sci. USA* **39**, 985–989.

Oepen, H. 1950. Über die Frühentwicklung von *Triton alpestris* bei Dunkelheit. *Arch. Entw.-Mech.* **144**, 322–328.

Ognev, I. F. 1910. Über Veränderungen in den Organen der Goldfische nach dreijährigem Verbleiben in Finsternis. *Biol. Zh.* **1**, 263–268.

Okada, E. W. and Ichikawa, M. 1956. Isolationsversuche zur Analyse der Knorpelbildung aus Neuralleistenzellen bei Anurenkeim. *Mem. Coll. Sci. Univ. Kyoto* B **23**, 27–36.

Oppenheimer, J. M. 1936. Transplantation experiments on developing teleosts (*Fundulus* and *Perca*). *J. exp. Zool.* **72**, 409–437.

— 1938. Potencies for differentiation in the teleostean germ ring. *J. exp. Zool.* **79**, 185–212.

— 1947. Organization of the teleost blastoderm. *Quart. Rev. Biol.* **22**, 105–118.

— 1949. Atypical pigment cell differentiation in embryonic teleostean grafts and isolates. *Proc. Nat. Ac. Sci. USA* **35**, 709–712.

— 1953. The development of transplanted fragments of *Fundulus* gastrulae. *Proc. Nat. Ac. Sci. USA* **39**, 1149–1152.

— 1955. Ectopic differentiation of ears in secondary embryos of *Fundulus*. *Proc. Nat. Ac. Sci. USA* **41**, 680–684.

Palm, E. 1947. On the occurrence in the retina of conditions corresponding to the blood-brain barrier. *Acta Ophth.* **25**, 29–35.

Pasteels, J. 1936. Études sur la gastrulation des Vertébrés méroblastiques I. Teleosteens. *Arch. Biol.* **47**, 205–308.

— 1939. La formation de la queue chez les Vertébrés. *Ann. Soc. Roy. Zool. Belg.* **70**, 33–51.

— 1940. Un aperçu comparatif de la gastrulation chez les Chordes. *Biol. Rev.* **15**, 59–106.

— 1942. New observations concerning the maps of presumptive areas of the young amphibian gastrula (*Amblystoma* and *Discoglossus*). *J. exp. Zool.* **89**, 255–282.

— 1948. Production d'embryons surnumeraires et de tératomes chez les amphibiens par la centrifugation. *C. R. Soc. biol.* **142**, 1320–1324.

— 1953a. Les effets de la centrifugation sur la blastula et la jeune gastrula des Amphibiens I. Méchanisme de la formation des organes secondaires aux dépens de l'ectoblaste *J. Embryol. exp. Morph.* **1**, 5–24.

— 1953. Les effets de la centrifugation sur la blastula et la jeune gastrula des Amphibiens II. Étude comparative de la sensibilité en fonction des stades et des espèces. *J. Embryol. exp. Morph.* **1**, 125–145.

— 1954. Les effets de la centrifugation sur la blastula et la jeune gastrula Amphibiens III. Interactions entre ébauches primaires et secondaires, IV. Discussion générale et conclusions. *J. Embryol. exp. Morph.* **2**, 122–148.

PIRIE, A. and VAN HEYNINGEN, R. 1956. *Biochemistry of the eye*. Blackwell Sci. Publ., Oxford.

POLEZHAEV, L. V. 1938. Explantationsversuche an Extremitätenanlagen. *Dokl. Akad. nauk SSSR* 21, 361–364.

RAVEN, C. P. 1931. Zur Entwicklung der Ganglienleiste I. Die Kinematik der Ganglienleistenentwicklung bei den Urodelen. *Arch. Entw.-Mech.* 125, 210–292.

— 1933. Zur Entwicklung der Ganglienleiste II. Über das Differenzierungsvermögen des Kopfganglienleistenmaterials von Urodelen. *Arch. Entw.-Mech.* 129, 179–198.

— 1937. Experiments on the origin of the sheath cells and sympathetic neuroblasts in amphibia. *J. comp. Neurol.* 67, 221–240.

— 1938. Über Potenz von Gastrulaektoderm nach 24stündigem Verweilen im äußeren Blatt der dorsalen Urmundlippe. *Arch. Entw.-Mech.* 137, 661–713.

REINBOLD, R. 1954. Différentiation organotypique, *in vitro*, de l'oeil chez l'embryon de poulet. *C. R. Soc. biol.* 148, 1493–1495.

— 1958. Régulation de l'oeil et régénération du cristallin chez l'embryon de poulet opéré en culture *in vitro*. *Arch. anat. micr. morph. exp.* 47, 341–357.

REYER, R. W. 1950. An experimental study of lens regeneration in Triturus viridiscens viridiscens. II. Lens development from the dorsal iris in absence of the embryonic lens. *J. exp. Zool.* 113, 317–353.

— 1954. Regeneration of the lens in the amphibian eye. *Quart. Rev. Biol.* 29, 1–46.

— 1956. Lens regeneration from homoplastic and heteroplastic implants of dorsal iris into the eye chamber of *Triturus viridiscens* and *Amblystoma punctatum*. *J. exp. Zool.* 133, 145–189.

ROCHON-DUVIGNEAUD, A. 1943. *Les yeux et la vision des Vertébrés*. Masson, Paris.

ROMANO, M. 1936. Le modificazione dell'occhio degli Anuri durante la metamorphosi. *Arch. Ital. Anat. Embr.* 36, 432–465.

RÜBSAAMEN, H. 1950. Die Wirkung des experimentellen Sauerstoffmangels auf die Entwicklung von Tritonkeim nach beendeter Gastrulation. *Arch. Entw.-Mech.* 144, 301–321.

— 1951. Die Beeinflussung der Kiemenentwicklung von Triton im experimentellen Sauerstoffmangel. *Beitr. path. Anat.* 111, 236–244.

RUGH, R. 1948. *Experimental Embryology*. Burgess Publ. Co., Minneapolis.

SALA, M. 1955. Distribution of activating and transforming influences in the archenteron roof during the induction of the nervous system in amphibians I. Distribution in cranio-caudal direction. *Proc. Nederl. Akad. Wetensch.* C 58, 635–647.

— 1956. The character of the local activations formed in sandwich explants of competent ectoderm containing neural formations induced by different cranio-caudal portions of the archenteron roof. *Proc. Nederl. Akad. Wetensch.* C 59, 661–667.

SAMBUICHI, H. 1957. The roles of the nucleus and the cytoplasm in development I. An intersubspecific hybrid frog, developed from a combination of *Rana nigromaculata nigromaculata* cytoplasm and a diploid nucleus of *Rana nigromaculata brevipoda*. *J. Sci. Hiroshima Univ.* B 17, 33–41.

SANFORD, K., EARLE, W. R. and LIKELY, G. D. 1948. The growth *in vitro* of single isolated tissue cells. *J. Nat. Cancer Inst.* 9, 229–246.

SATO, T. 1953. Über die Ursachen des Ausbleibens der Linsenregeneration und zugleich über die linsenbildende Fähigkeit des Pigmentepithels bei der Anuren. *Arch. Entw.-Mech.* 146, 487–514.

SAUNDERS, J. W. 1948. The proximo-distal sequence of origin of the parts of the chick wing and the role of the ectoderm. *J. exp. Zool.* 108, 363–403.

SAXÉN, L. and TOIVONEN, S. 1956. Inductive action of normal and leukemic bone-marrow of the rat. *Ann. Med. exper. Fenn.* 34, 235–241.

SCHECHTMAN, A. M. 1952. Physical and chemical changes in the circulating blood. *Ann. N.-Y. Ac. Sc.* 55, 85–98.

1955. Ontogeny of the blood and related antigens and their significance for the theory of differentiation. *Biological Specificity and Growth*, 3–31. Princeton Univ. Press.

SCHMALHAUSEN, I. I. 1938. *Organism as a Whole in Individual and Historical Development*. Acad. Sci. SSSR Press, Moscow/Leningrad.

SCHMALHAUSEN, O. I. 1940. The development of ear vesicles in the absence of hindbrain in amphibians. *Dokl. Akad. nauk SSSR* 28, 276–279.

1947. The dependence of formative reactions of the embryo of *Triturus vulgaris* from the stage of development after transplantation of pieces of fixed tissues. *Dokl. Akad. nauk SSSR* 58, 1841–1844.

1950. Localization and development of nasal rudiments in connection with the question of their origin in vertebrates. *Dokl. Akad. nauk SSSR* 74, 1045–1048.

SCHMIDT, G. A. and RAGOSINA, M. N. 1937. Einfluss eines sekundären Organisators auf primäres embryonales Material. *Zool. Anz.* 120, 143–146.

SEIDEL, F. 1932. Die Potensen der Furchungskerne im Libellenei und ihre Rolle bei der Aktivierung des Bildungszentrums. *Arch. Entw.-Mech.* 126, 213–276.

SHEINA, A. P. 1940. Comparative study of lens-forming properties of body epithelium at different stages in the development of *Rana temporaria*, *Rana esculenta*, and *Rana arvalis*. *Dokl. Akad. nauk SSSR* 42, 72–74.

1944. Comparative study of lens-forming properties of body of pieces of fixed tissue epithelium at different stages of development in *Bombina bombina* and *Amblystoma mexicanum*. *Dokl. Akad. nauk SSSR* 44, 232–236.

SMITHBERG, M. 1954. The origin and development of the tail in the frog, *Rana pipiens. J. exp. Zool.* 127, 397–425.

SPEMANN, H. 1901. Über Korrelationen in der Entwicklung des Auges. *Verh. anat. Ges.* 15, 61–79.

1906. Über eine neue Methode der embryonalen Transplantation. *Verh. dtsch. zool. Ges.* 196–202.

1912. Zur Entwicklung des Wirbeltierauges. *Zool. Jb. Physiol.* 32, 1–98.

1924. Über Organisatoren in der tierischen Entwicklung. *Naturwiss.* 12, 1092–1094.

1928. Die Entwicklung seitlicher und dorsoventraler Keimhälften bei verzögerter Kernversorgung. *Z. wiss. Zool.* 132, 105–134.

1931. Über den Anteil von Implantat und Wirtskeim an der Orientierung und Beschaffenheit der induzierten Embryonalanlage. *Arch. Entw.-Mech.* 123, 390–517.

SPEMANN, H. 1936. *Experimentelle Beiträge zu einer Theorie der Entwicklung.* Springer, Berlin.

SPEMANN, H. und MANGOLD, H. 1924. Über Induktion von Embryonalanlagen durch Implantation artfremder Organisatoren. *Arch. mikr. Anat. u. Entw.-Mech.* **100**, 599−638.

SPEMANN, H. und SCHOTTÉ, O. 1932. Über xenoplastische Transplantation als Mittel zur Analyse der embryonalen Induktion. *Naturwiss.* **20**, 463−467.

SPIEGELMAN, S. 1945. Physiological competition as a regulatory mechanism in morphogenesis. *Quart. Rev. Biol.* **20**, 121−146.

—— 1946. Nuclear and cytoplasmic factors controlling enzymatic constitution. *Symp. Quant. Biol.* **11**, 256−277.

—— 1948. Differentiation as a controlled production of unique enzyme patterns. *Symp. Soc. Exp. Biol.* **2**, 286−325.

SPOFFORD, W. K. 1948. Observations on the posterior part of the neural plate in *Amblystoma.* II. The inductive effect of the intact posterior part of the chorda-mesodermal axis on competent prospective ectoderm. *J. exp. Zool.* **107**, 123−163.

STONE, L. S. 1922. Experiments on development of the cranial ganglia and the lateral-line sense organs in *Amblystoma. J. exp. Zool.* **35**, 421−496.

—— 1929. Experiments showing the role of migrating neural crest (mesectoderm) in the formation of head skeleton and loose connective tissue in *Rana palustris. Arch. Entw.-Mech.* **118**, 40−77.

—— 1931. Induction of the ear by the medulla and its relation to experiments on the lateralis system in amphibia. *Science* **74**, 577.

—— 1950a. Neural retina degeneration following by regeneration from surviving retinal pigment cells in grafted adult salamander eyes. *Anat. Rec.* **106**, 89−109.

—— 1950b. The role of retinal pigment cells in regenerating neural retinae of adult salamander eyes. *J. exp. Zool.* **113**, 9−31.

STONE, L. S. and SAPIR, P. 1940. Experimental studies on the regeneration of the lens in the eye of anurans, urodeles and fishes. *J. exp. Zool.* **85**, 71−101.

STONE, L. S. and STEINITZ, H. 1957. Regeneration of neural retina and lens from retina pigment cell grafts in adult newts. *J. exp. Zool.* **135**, 301−318.

STROEVA, O. G. 1950a. Stages in the formation of fins in amphibian larvae. *Dokl. Akad. nauk SSSR* **70**, 145−147.

—— 1950b. On the correlation in the development of the fin and body of amphibian larvae. *Dokl. Akad. nauk* **70**, 1093−1096.

—— 1952. Experimental and comparative research of early stages of development of organs of locomotion in some vertebrates. Diss., Mosc. State Univ.

—— 1956a. Transformation of pigment epithelium into retina under influence of indophenol in tadpoles of *Rana arvalis. Dokl. Akad. nauk SSSR* **108**, 562−564.

—— 1956b. Experimental study of the conditions determining the development of the pigment epithelium and the neural retina in mammals. *Dokl. Akad. nauk SSSR* **109**, 657−660.

—— 1956c. Studies of the regenerative power of the retina in adult *Bombina* and rats. *Izv. Akad. nauk SSSR, ser. biol.* No. **5**, 76−84.

STROEVA, O. G. 1960. Experimental analysis of the eye morphogenesis in mammals. *J. Embryol. exp. Morph.* **8**, 349–368.

TAKAYA, H. 1953a. On the notochord-forming potency of the prechordal plate in *Triturus* gastrulae. *Proc. Japan Acad.* **29**, 374–380.

1953b On the loss of the notochord-forming potency in the prechordal plate of the Triturus gastrula. *Annot. Zool. japon*, **26**, 202–207.

1955a. Formation of the brain from the prospective spinal cord of amphibian embryos. *Proc. Japan Acad.* **31**, 360–365.

1955b. Thermal influence upon the inducing specificity of the organizer. *Proc. Japan. Acad.* **31**, 366–371.

1956. Two types of neural differentiation produced in connection with mesenchymal tissue. *Proc. Japan Acad.* **32**, 282–286.

TERENTIEV, I. B. 1941. Zur Frage über die Bedeutung der Ganglienleiste in der Entwicklung des dorsalen Flossensaums bei Urodelen. *Dokl. Akad. nauk SSSR* **31**, 84–86.

TERNI, T. 1934. Studio sperimentali della capacita pinnoformativa dei cercini midollari. *Arch. Ital. Anat. Embr.* **33**, 667–692.

TIEDEMANN, H. 1959. Neue Ergebnisse zur Frage nach der chemischen Natur der Induktionsstoffe beim Organisatoreffekt Spemanns. *Naturwiss.* **46**, 613–623.

TOIVONEN, S. 1940. Über die Leistungsspezifität der abnormen Induktoren im Implantatversuch bei *Triton*. *Ann. Ac. Sci. Fenn.* A 55 (6), 1–150.

1945. Zur Frage der Induktion selbständiger Linsen durch abnorme Induktoren im Implantatversuch bei *Triton*. *Ann. Zool. Soc. Fenn. Vamano* **11**, 1–28.

1950. Stoffliche Induktoren. *Rev. Suisse Zool.* **57**, suppl. 1, 51–56.

1953. Knochenmark als mesodermaler Induktor im Implantatversuch bei *Triturus. Arch. Soc. Zool. Bot. Fenn. Vanamo* **7**, 113–121.

1954. The inducing action of the bone-marrow of the guinea-pig after alcohol and heat treatment in implantation and explantation experiments with embryos of *Triturus. J. Embryol. exp. Morph.* **2**, 239–244.

1958. Dependence of the cellular transformation of competent ectoderm on temporal relationships in the induction process. *J. Embryol. exp. Morph.* **6**, 479–485.

TOIVONEN, S. and SAXÉN, L. 1955. Über die Induktion des Neuralrohrs bei bei Trituruskeimen als simultane Leistung des Leber- und Knochenmarkgewebes von Meeresschweinchen. *Ann. Ac. Sci. Fenn.* A IV, **30**, 1–30.

TOKIN, B. P. 1943. The phenomenon of "organizers" and chemical passions of embryologists. *Zh. obshch. biol.* **4**, 3–14.

TSCHUMI, P. A. 1947. The growth of the hindlimb bud of *Xenopus laevis* and its dependence upon the epidermis. *J. Anat.* **91**, 149–173.

TUMANISHVILI, G. D. DZHANDIERI, K. M. and SVANIDZE, I. K. 1956. Specific stimulation of growth of organs of the chick embryo with tissue extracts. *Dokl. Akad. nauk SSSR* **106**, 1107–1109.

TWITTY, V. C. 1940. Size-controlling factors. *Growth*, suppl. 4, 109–120.

1945. The developmental analysis of specific pigment patterns. *J. exp. Zool.* **100**, 141–178.

TWITTY, V. C. and BODENSTEIN, D. 1941. Experiments on the determination problem I. The roles of ectoderm and neural crest in the development of the dorsal fin in Amphibia. *J. exp. Zool.* **86**, 343–362.

TYLER, A. 1935. On the energetics of differentiation II. A comparison of the rates of development of giant and normal sea-urchin embryos. *Biol. Bull.* **68**, 451–460.

UMANSKI, E. 1935. Über die gegenseitige Vertretbarkeit präsumptiver Anlagen der Rückenmark- und Hirnteile bei den Amphibien. *Zool. Anz.* **110**, 25–30.

VAHS, W. 1957. Experimentelle Untersuchungen am *Triturus*-Keim über die stofflichen Mittel abnormer Induktoren. *Arch. Entw.-Mech.* **149**, 339–364.

VOGT, W. 1929. Gestaltungsanalyse am Amphibienkeim mit örtlicher Vital-färbung II. Gasrulation und Mesodermbildung bei Urodelen und Anuren. *Arch. Entw.-Mech.* **120**, 385–706.

WACHS, H. 1920. Restitution des Auges nach Extirpation von Retina und Linse bei Tritonen. *Arch. Entw.-Mech.* **46**, 328–390.

WADDINGTON, C. H. 1936. The origin of competence for lens formation in the Amphibia. *J. exp. Biol.* **13**, 86–91.

WADDINGTON, C. H. and PANTELOURIS, E. M. 1953. Transplantation of nuclei in newt's eggs. *Nature* **172**, 1050–1051.

WAECHTER, H. 1953. Die Induktionsfähigkeit der Gehirnplatte bei Urodelen und ihr medianlaterales Gefälle. *Arch. Entw.-Mech.* **146**, 201–274.

WAGNER, R. and MITCHELL, H. 1955. *Genetics and Metabolism.* Chapman and Hall, London.

WALDER, P. 1950. Über das Wachstum der Kopforgane und die Entstehung von Mikrophthalmie bei isolierten Kopfstücken und zirkulationslosen Keimen von Triton alpestris. *Acta zool.* **31**, 187–231.

WALLS, G. L. 1942. *The Vertebrate Eye and its Adaptive Radiation.* Cranbrook Inst. Sci. Bloomfield Hills.

WARKANY, J. and SCHRAFFENBERGER, E. 1946. Congenital malformations induced by maternal vitamin E definiency I. Defects of the eye. *Arch. Ophth.* **35**, 150–169.

WASNETZOV, V. V. 1946. Divergence and adaptation in ontogeny, *Zool. Zh.* **25**, 185–200.

WEISS, P. 1934. Secretory activity of the inner layer of the embryonic mid-brain of the chick, as revealed by tissue culture. *Anat. Rec.* **58**, 299–302.

— 1935. The so-called organizer and the problem of organization in amphibian development. *Physiol. Rev.* **15**, 641–674.

WEISS, P. and ANDRES, G. 1952. Experiments on the fate of embryonic cells (chick) disseminated by the vascular route. *J. exp. Zool.* **121**, 449–487.

WEISZ, P. B. 1951. A general mechanism of differentiation based on morpho-genetic studies in Ciliates. *Am. Nat.* **85**, 293–311.

— 1954. Morphogenesis in Protozoa. *Quart. Rev. Biol.* **29**, 207–229.

WILLS, I. A. 1936. The respiratory rate of developing Amphibia with special reference to sex differentiation. *J. exp. Zool.* **73**, 481–510.

WINNIKOV, J. A. 1945. Explantation of neural folds of amphibians. *Dokl. Akad. nauk SSSR* **48**, 314–317.

— 1947a. Experimental studies of the development of presumptive eye rudiment. *Izv. Akad. nauk SSSR, ser. biol.* No. 5, 633–664.

— 1947b. *The Retina of the Vertebrate Eye.* Medgiz, Moscow.

Wislocki, G. B. and Ladman, A. J. 1955. The demonstration of a blood-ocular barrier in the albino rat by means of the intravitam deposition of silver. *J. biophys. biochem. Cytol.* **1**, 501–510.

von Woellwarth, C. 1952. Die Induktionsstufen des Gehirns. *Arch. Entw.-Mech.* **145**, 582–668.

— 1956. Die induzierende Wirkung von rohem, flüssigem Hühnerembryonal-extrakt auf Gastrula-Ektoderm von *Triton. Arch. Entw.-Mech.* **148**, 504–517.

Woerdeman, M. W. 1938. Inducing capacity of the embryonic eye. *Proc. Nederl. Akad. Wetensch.* C **41**, 336–343.

— 1953. Serological methods in the study of morphogenesis. *Arch. neerl. Zool.* **10**, suppl. 1, 144–164.

Yamada, T. 1937. Der Determinationszustand des Rumpfmesoderms im Molch-keim nach der Gastrulation. *Arch. Entw.-Mech.* **137**, 151–270.

— 1939a. Über den Einfluß von Wirtsalter auf die Differenzierung von ver-pflanztem Ursegmentmaterial des Molchembryo. *Japan. J. Zool.* **8**, 265–283.

— 1939b. Wechselseitige Induktion zwischen Merullaranlage und Ursegment-material des Molchkeimes, dargestellt an zusammengesetzten Isolaten. *Fol. anat. japon.* **18**, 569–571.

— 1940. Beeinflussung der Differenzierungsleistung des isolierten Mesoderms von Molchkeimen durch zugefügtes Chorda und Neuralmaterial. *Fol. anat. japon.* **19**, 131–197.

— 1950. Dorsalization of the ventral marginal zone of the *Triturus* gastrula I. *Biol. Bull.* **98**, 98–121.

— 1958a. Induction of specific differentiation by samples of proteins and nucleo-proteins in the isolated ectoderm of Triturus-gastrulae. *Experientia* **14**, 81–87.

— 1958b. Embryonic induction. *The Chemical Basis of Development*, 217–238. J. Hopkins Press, Baltimore.

Yamada, T. and Takata, K. 1955a. An analysis of spino-caudal induction by the guinea-pig kidney in the isolated ectoderm of the *Triturus* gastrula. *J. exp. Zool.* **128**, 291–331.

— 1955b. Effect of trypsin and chymotrypsin in the inducing ability of the kidney and its fractions. *Exp. Cello. Res.*, suppl. 3, 402–413.

Yntema, C. L. 1933. Experiments on the determination of the ear ectoderm in the embryo of *Amblystoma punctatum. J. exp. Zool.* **65**, 317–357.

— 1939. Self-differentiation of heterotopic ear ectoderm in the embryo of *Amblystoma punctatum. J. exp. Zool.* **80**, 1–17.

— 1950. An analysis of induction of the ear from foreign ectoderm in the salamander embryo. *J. exp. Zool.* **113**, 211–243.

— 1955. Ear and Nose. *Analysis of Development*, 415–428. Saunders, Phila-delphia and London.

Zavadovsky, M. M. 1941. *Contradictory Interaction between Organs in the Body of the Developing Animal.* Moscow State Univ. Press.

Zwilling, E. 1949. The role of epithelial components in the developmental origin of the "wingless" syndrome of chick embryos. *J. exp. Zool.* **111**, 175–187.

— 1955. Ectoderm-mesoderm relationship in the development of the chick embryo limb bud. *J. exp. Zool.* **128**, 423–441.

— 1956. Interaction between limb bud ectoderm and mesoderm in the chick embryo I, II. *J. exp. Zool.* **132**, 157–187.